THE MOON AND THE PLANETS

THE
MOON
AND THE
PLANETS

BY JOSEF SADIL

ILLUSTRATED BY LUDĚK PEŠEK

PAUL HAMLYN

LONDON

Translated into English by Káča Poláčková
Graphic design by P. Pospíšil and V. Rada
Designed and produced by Artia for
PAUL HAMLYN LTD
Westbook House • Fulham Broadway • London
© 1963 by Artia
Printed in Czechoslovakia
S 1325

CONTENTS

The Moon and the Planets	9
List of Plates	21
The Moon	25
Venus	93
Mercury	115
Mars	125
Jupiter	145
Saturn	157
Uranus	173
Neptune	177
Pluto	181

THE MOON AND THE PLANETS

If you look out into the sky at night, at first glance all the twinkling objects in it seem to be hanging motionless.

But if you observe, night after night, it becomes apparent that a few of those objects are moving; and after several weeks of watching some have plainly vanished while fresh ones have risen above the horizon.

Man noticed this feature of the Universe a very long time ago—certainly as long ago as 2000 B.C.—and quickly began labelling all that he saw so that he could more easily keep track of it.

Prominent stars were given special names, like Aldebaran, Sirius or Capella. Many were grouped within the outlines of imaginary figures such as The Archer, The Plough, The Lion or The Scorpion.

Man observed that most of the stars and clumps of stars did not change their position in relation to each other; so he classified these 'stellae fixae'—fixed stars.

The others he called 'stellae errantes'—wandering stars. For they clearly moved about the sky, sometimes stopping and even, occasionally, going backwards.

As he studied these more closely with the aid of instruments, he was able to determine that their movement had a definite pattern—that they were all revolving round the Sun.

They were, in fact, Planets.

1. The apparent motion of the stars over Lomnický štít in the High Tatras. (Photo by J. Klepeta.)

2. *Apparent conjunction of the planets Jupiter and Uranus on January 24, 1955. (Photo by A. Rückl.)*

3. *Side view of Galaxy NGC 891 in Andromeda. We and our Sun, along with 150 thousand million other stars, are part of a similar lens-shaped cloud of stars—our Galaxy. It measures 85,000 light years across (one light year is equal to about 5.9 million million miles) and is 7,000 light years thick through the centre. Our Sun is about 25,000 light years from the centre of the Galaxy, and makes one revolution around this centre once in 250 million years. (Photo—Mt Wilson.)*

There are nine planets orbiting our Sun, one of them being the Earth we live on—although this fact was not realised until the 16th century when an astronomer named Nicholas Copernicus proved it so.

Together the nine comprise the Solar System.

Modern astronomy is now satisfied that our Solar System, far from being the only one of its kind in the Universe, is just one among thousands of millions of similar systems: and that our Sun—fierce, fiery, all-dominating disc that it may seem—is just an ordinary star like those countless billions of others we see as pale points of light in the night sky.

Stars are huge, glowing gaseous spheres. Planets are much smaller, solid bodies.

Inside stars, tremendous pressures and temperatures build up. In the centre of our sun, for instance, the temperature is estimated to be about 14,500,000 degrees Centigrade and this is cool by comparison with some stars.

Under these conditions, reactions between atoms of gases—such as hydrogen—which are present inside the stars, occur spontaneously, with the result that huge amounts of radiant energy are released.

Planets, because of their smaller size, lack the pressure and temperature necessary to trigger and keep going such reactions. So they have to derive most of their energy from the sun around which they are revolving.

On Earth, for example, the coal we use, the food we eat, the petrol we burn all originate from the sun.

The surfaces of planets are dark. They only shine because they are reflecting light from their parent star.

So far, we on Earth have only found it possible to observe visually eight planets—our companions in the Solar System.

But other, as yet invisible lumps—which appear to be planets—are suspected to be travelling around some of the stars nearest to us in the heavens.

The smallest of these objects has been estimated to be about eight times larger than our system's largest planet, which is Jupiter.

We believe, therefore, that there are probably billions of planets in the Universe, just as there are certainly billions of suns.

Why do they exist?

A theory widely held today suggests that the Planets are simply embryo stars, which have not yet merged to form one denser clump. They are thought to have originated—like their parent suns—from the gradual accumulation of clouds of dust and gas in interstellar space.

They are of particular interest to us because they seem to be the only possible bearers of life in the Universe.

Even so, they must fulfil certain conditions to do this.

They must be massive enough to retain an atmosphere, although this need not necessarily have the same composition as our air on Earth.

They must remain within a certain maximum and minimum distance from their central star.

They must have favourable light and heat conditions.

Finally, if the life is to be in a form recognisable to Man, they must have some liquid water.

Two planets have always seemed more likely to contain life than the others—Mars and Venus. Both became immediate targets when the United States and the Soviet Union developed their rocketry to the point at which physical exploration of the Universe could begin.

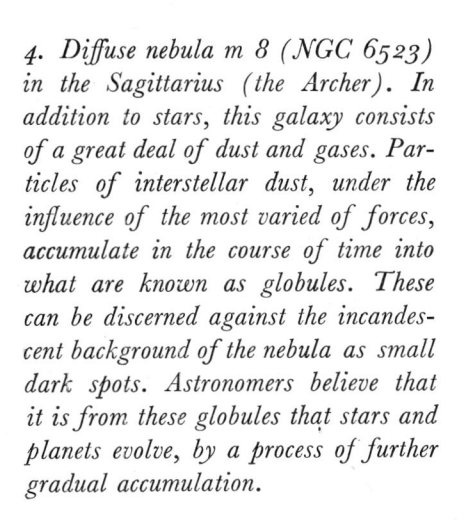

4. Diffuse nebula m 8 (NGC 6523) in the Sagittarius (the Archer). In addition to stars, this galaxy consists of a great deal of dust and gases. Particles of interstellar dust, under the influence of the most varied of forces, accumulate in the course of time into what are known as globules. These can be discerned against the incandescent background of the nebula as small dark spots. Astronomers believe that it is from these globules that stars and planets evolve, by a process of further gradual accumulation.

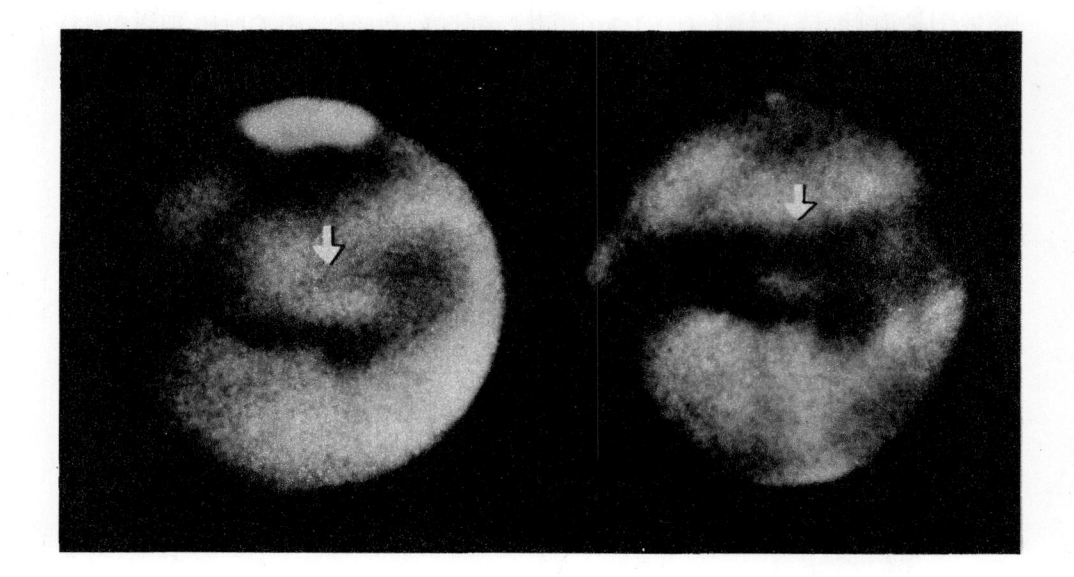

5. *The surface of the planet Mars is the scene of significant seasonal changes. The picture at left shows the planet at a time when spring is arriving on the southern (upper) hemisphere. The white southern polar cap is still fairly extensive, but is starting to shrink rapidly. The dark area in the southern subtropical region called Pandorae Fretum (arrow) is still not very apparent. In summer (see photo, right) the polar cap disappears entirely, and Pandorae Fretum appears as a wide dark stripe. (Photo by E.C. Slipher, Lowell Observatory.)*

But the initial results of the probing by spacecraft—backed up by optical telescopes lofted above the distorting haze of our atmosphere—have come as something of a shock.

Neither planet appears to have conditions as favourable to life as was previously believed. But the quest goes on. For Man is only at the beginning of a new period of understanding.

The recency of our knowledge about the planets can be gauged by the fact that until the 16th century only five planets had been recognised. These were Mars, Venus, Mercury, Jupiter and Saturn.

Uranus was not discovered until 1781, Neptune not before 1846 and Pluto as late as 1930.

Today the quality of our optical instruments and the availability of radar make us confident that no more lurk in our Solar System.

The nine can be divided, according to certain physical and chemical characteristics, into two groups—the *inferior* planets, which except for Pluto are closest to the sun, and the outer or *superior* ones.

The Earth is an inner planet. So are Mars, Venus and Mercury. They are all fairly small, with diameters ranging from 3,008 to 7,926 miles. Their average density is quite high—5.5 to 5.9 grams of matter to each cubic centimetre of space occupied.

They have comparatively thin atmospheres and take a relatively long time to rotate about their axes.

The Earth, for instance, makes one revolution every 23 hours 56 minutes 4 seconds—not 24 hours as is popularly believed. Mars goes round once in 24 hours 37 minutes and 22.7 seconds; Mercury in 87 days 23 hours 15 minutes and 44 seconds.

Until recently it was thought that Venus—which has always been hidden from our eyes by strange clouds near its surface—rotated about once a fortnight. But the U.S. Mariner spacecraft which passed within 21,000 miles of the planet in December 1962 checked this and found the figure hopelessly wrong.

Venus—as subsequent radar measurements confirmed—turns very, very slowly: once, in fact, in about 250 days.

The outer, or superior planets—Jupiter, Saturn, Uranus and Neptune—are bigger. Their diameters range from 27,700 to 88,698 miles. Their average density, by contrast, is fairly low—only 0.68 to 1.58 grams to every cubic centimetre.

These planets have very dense atmospheres—believed to consist mainly of hydrogen—and revolve much more rapidly about their axes. They take from 9 hours 50 minutes to just under 16 hours to go round once.

Why are the two groups of planets so different?

It is thought that their individual peculiarities were stamped on them right at the birth of our Solar System.

There are at least thirteen major theories to explain how the planets came into being, ranging from one which claims that they were part of the Sun torn out by the pull of a passing star, to one which says they were local concentrations of gas and dust.

6. *The planet Jupiter. (Photo—Mt Palomar.)*

7. *The planet Saturn. (Photo—Yerkes' Observatory.)*

But the one I favour goes like this.

Picture—if you can—the Sun forming itself out of a huge cloud of dust and gas which is swirling in tighter and tighter.

The temperature inside this mass begins to rise. It reaches such fantastic heights that atomic reactions are triggered off. The nuclei, or cores, of the atoms begin fusing together, liberating immense energy in the process.

The Sun starts to radiate part of the energy as waves of light—some visible, some invisible, in what is called the 'infra-red' region of the colour spectrum.

These rays bring about definite physical and chemical changes in the cloud still surrounding the young Sun. This cloud contains a high proportion of solid matter—dust and bigger debris of meteor size. It contains too, a lot of 'loose' atoms and compounds and elements, the chief one being hydrogen.

The rays act on the debris. The 'pressure' of the Sun's radiation forces the lightest debris and gases to the outer edges of the cloud.

The inner part becomes rich in heavier elements: iron, silicon and oxygen, for example. Only small quantities of light elements survive in this region, as it begins to bond together into balls.

The outer part—far from the warm body of the Sun and screened by the inner curtain of matter—freezes.

The light-weight elements there—hydrogen, helium and similar gases—freeze hard on the dust particles: and these gradually accumulate into balls too.

That, then, is my simple model for the formation of the two types of planet.

It shows why the inner planets are heavier—because they were made from heavy elements bonding together near the hot Sun: and why the outer ones, with light-weight materials and gases in their structure, are of low density but clothed in thick atmospheres.

The one unknown quantity is Pluto. By its mass, it should be classified with the inner planets, for it is only slightly smaller than the Earth.

Yet it is the outermost of all, moving around the Sun in a huge concentric orbit at a mean distance of 3,666 million miles.

Only the most powerful telescopes can locate it, so it is no surprise that it went undetected for so long and is still something of a mystery.

Farther out even than Pluto there are looser clumps of matter. They too move around the Sun and are therefore part of the Solar System.

They are the *comets*.

A comet consists of a core of all solid particles of frozen gas, surrounded by a hazy envelope called a *coma*.

Unlike the planets, whose orbits around the Sun are more circular, most comets follow long elliptical or egg-shaped paths. Some take hundreds of years to go round once.

If a comet comes close enough to the Sun in its orbit its surface temperature begins to rise rapidly. The frozen gases in its core—mainly ammonia, carbon tetrachloride, water and carbon monoxide—begin to evaporate. Ultra-violet radiation from the Sun breaks them down into less complex molecules and the result is that an atmosphere or *coma* forms around the whole.

This *coma* can enlarge the size of the comet by as much as ten times—say to a diameter of 60,000 miles, which is nearly as big as Jupiter or Saturn.

Because the *coma* absorbs radiation, it begins to fluoresce, or shine by its own light. It is then visible to us on Earth.

In the process of evaporation some of the particles and frozen gases from the core burst through the *coma* and are forced away from the comet in the opposite direction to the Sun—as if the Sun were blowing at the comet.

They stream out behind it as a tail, which glows vividly. The tail can stretch out a long way. For instance, one comet seen in 1843 is estimated to have had a tail between 150 and 200 million miles long.

Comets, therefore, are quite easy to track with telescopes. Indeed, the orbits of nearly 600 have now

8. Mrkos' comet, 1957. (Photo by Alan McClure, Los Angeles.)

been plotted fairly accurately, and each year between five and ten new ones are located, often by amateur astronomers.

The nucleus of a comet is unlikely to weigh more than a few hundred thousand tons, but if one were to collide with Earth it would cause a catastrophe.

There is some doubt as to whether the object which fell in Siberia on June 30th 1908 was a meteorite or a comet, but whichever it was it caused a tremendous explosion. Seismographs as far away as Jena in Germany registered the collision, and it destroyed forests forty miles from the centre of the impact.

Our first picture illustrates the collision of the Earth with the nucleus of a comet as viewed from tens of thousands of miles away. Such collisions are rare occurrences, fortunately. But collisions between Earth and small *meteors*—many of which are remnants of disintegrated comets—are very frequent.

Meteors are made of stony material or metal. They orbit the Sun, often huddled together in billions, as a stream, or individually.

If they meet our dense atmosphere they burn from the resulting friction. At night they show up brilliantly as 'shooting stars'.

According to various estimates, between 20 million and 5,000 million small meteors plunge into our atmosphere each day.

This matter, which enters the Earth's air blanket, weighs between 1,000 and 10,000 tons—equal to a yearly increase in the Earth's weight of almost six pounds for every square mile.

Small meteors usually lose all, or at least 90 per cent of their original cosmic speed—between five and forty-five miles per second—as they come through the atmosphere, and rarely do much damage.

But the larger ones are not slowed so much by resistance of the air and sometimes hit the Earth's surface with violence. They can cause a great explosion and form a deep crater where they fall.

Something like this happened in Arizona several thousand years ago. An immense meteor, about 260 feet in diameter and weighing some 2,000,000 tons, formed a crater 3,870 feet wide and 560 feet deep.

It must have been travelling at more than twelve miles a second before it entered the atmosphere.

Any meteors that reach the ground are termed *meteorites*.

In addition to meteors, there are thousands of larger lumps of matter hurtling around the Sun—mostly in the region of space between the orbits of Mars and Jupiter.

These are known as *asteroids*.

They range in size from 529 miles across to about half a mile. The biggest are called *planetoids*, and the smallest *microplanets*.

Some 6,000 asteroids have been discovered to date, but scores are added to the list each year. If all of them were put together, it is estimated, their mass would still only total about a thousandth of that of the Earth.

Analysis of the way their brightness varies has shown that they are not spheres but jagged bodies—probably broken-up lumps of rock.

The belief is that they are remnants of several planets—probably about the size of Mercury—which used to orbit between Mars and Jupiter.

Due to their nearness to the great planet Jupiter, according to the theory, their orbits were disturbed by gravity; suddenly they collided, breaking into millions of bits, some big, some tiny.

Further collisions occur all the time, so it is possible that the total of asteroids may still be increasing.

Many asteroids may, in the course of their orbits about the Sun, approach the Earth more closely than does the Moon. For instance, the asteroid Hermes—a huge rock about 2,500 feet in diameter and discovered in 1937—can approach the Earth to within 220,000 miles.

The most prominent asteroid is named Ceres. It was discovered in 1801 and can be seen with the naked eye.

Thus we can see that the vast blackness of our Solar System is filled with countless pieces and varieties of solid matter.

But there is one type of object that we have not yet mentioned—*moons*, or *satellites*, as they are called.

Moons revolve around most of the planets in the Solar System. The Earth has one, Mars has two, Jupiter twelve, Saturn nine, Uranus five, Neptune two—a total of thirty-one moons.

It is quite probable that Pluto should be classified as a moon too—a former satellite of Neptune. That would explain its smaller size, relatively great density, rare atmosphere, highly eccentric orbit and the fact that it rotates slowly in 6.39 days.

9. The Earth's Moon, shortly before it is full. (At this stage, we say that the moon is gibbous.) (Photo by V. Mlejnek, Observatory Úpice, Czechoslovakia.)

10. Jupiter and its moons, February 11th, 1955. (From left to right, Jupiter's moons are visible as follows: III, IV, II, I, at 20 hours 50 minutes UT (Universal Time.) (Photo by A. Rükl.)

The larger of these thirty-one satellites probably began as planets in their own right, but because they were in the proximity of bigger planets they were affected by gravitational pull.

Their small size can be explained—if we revert to our model for creation for a moment—by the fact that their large neighbours apparently used up most of the 'building matter' in the cloud.

This may be how the Earth and the Moon came to be linked together: and why four of Jupiter's moons—those named Io, Europa, Ganymede and Callisto—are much larger than the rest.

The smaller moons—particularly any which orbit their parent planet in a clockwise direction—are probably asteroids which have become trapped in the gravitational fields of the bigger bodies.

Until the end of the 19th century, investigation of the Solar System and the planets in particular was mainly limited to observation through telescopes. Any details seen of their surfaces were recorded.

This early study of the planets was therefore given the name of *planetography*, because it paralleled geography—the study of the Earth.

At the beginning of the 20th century scientists began using new physical methods. *Photometry* gave them a way to measure the brightness of stars. *Polarimetry* enabled them to draw conclusions about the condition and surface structure of the planets by the degree of polarisation in the light coming from them. *Spectrum analysis* permitted the different elements on the planets to be identified by the various light colours they emitted. And *photography* was used more and more widely.

An entirely new field of science grew up: planetary physics. And as the work became more and more complex, *planetology*—the equivalent of geology on Earth—and *astrobotanics* were born.

Finally, the highly specialised field of *astrobiology*—the study of the possibility of life existing on other planets—attracted many enthusiasts.

These studies are still growing in importance. They will doubtless continue to break up into further specialised fields as more information becomes available to scientists. The trend now is to concentrate on each planet separately—on its physics, basic composition, meteorology, etc. This is largely the result of transition from 'old-fashioned' passive methods of observation from the Earth to active observation with the aid of spacecraft, satellites above the atmosphere, and rocket probes.

Natural scientists, such as geophysicists, mineralogists and petrographers are already widening their research interests to include other planets.

Their conclusions, which in the past have only been valid on Earth, will gradually become universally applicable as more and more information is gleaned for comparison.

From clues found so far it is possible to get a picture of the outer planets as being very much in their original form—internally and externally. But the *inner* four have clearly undergone a major change since birth.

One can visualise a process similar to that in a blast-furnace having occurred.

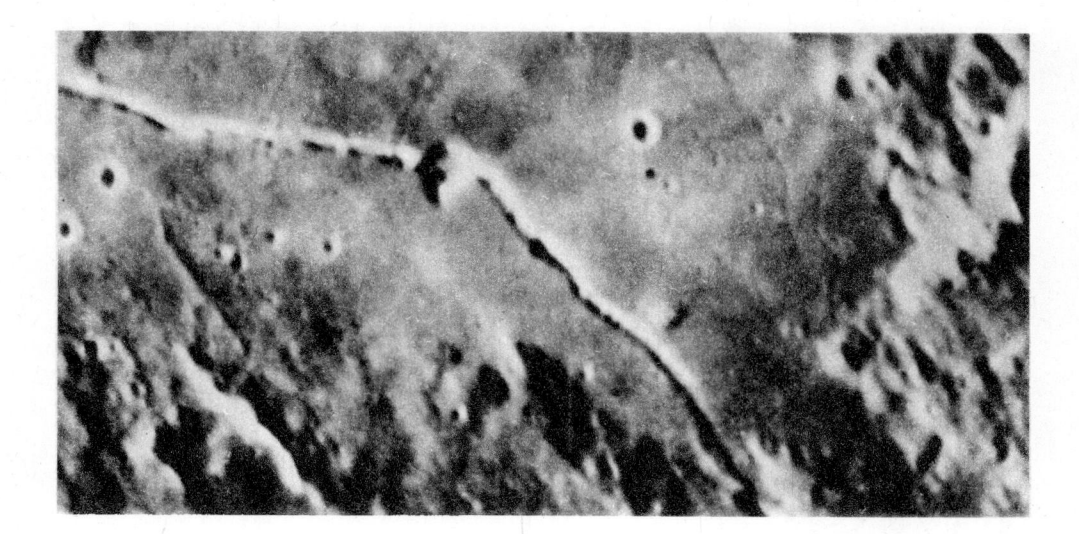

11. The Hygnius Cleft (Photo—Pic du Midi). See our reconstruction, Plate 11.

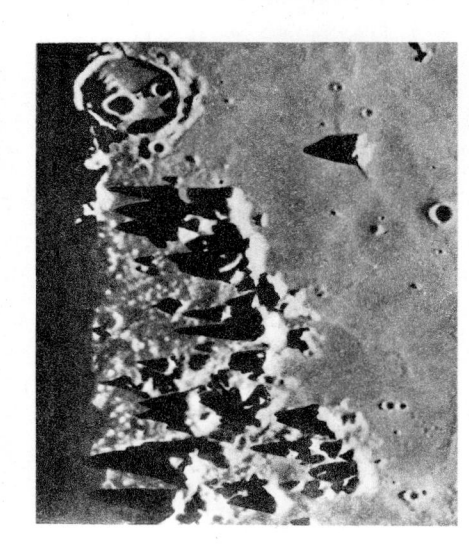

12. Alpine Valley on the Moon, at sunrise (left) and sunset. (Photo—Mt Wilson.) See our reconstruction, Plate 12.

The accumulation of heat—released in the course of disintegration of various radioactive elements, such as uranium, thorium and potassium, and by the compounding of free elements—caused their cores to melt. The heavy iron compounds were forced to the depths and the lighter silicates rose to the surface like slag.

The primitive surfaces of these planets began to undergo fairly rapid changes. Sedimentation occurred. Volcanic activity started up. The primary atmospheres changed as well and were replaced by secondary ones.

On at least one planet Life began.

But here the imagination usually takes over. Man is often tempted to describe the unknown and the undiscovered as something fantastic, terrifying, and quite different from anything he has seen in the past. The result has been a long line of science-fiction and horror-fiction stories.

In the middle-ages, story-tellers filled the then unexplored oceans with fabulous monsters which all bore a strange resemblance to man or some known species of animal. Hence we had the mermaid, the serpent, the sea-devil, the sea-horse, the sea-ape and sea-monk.

Until recently, fiction writers followed this trend by populating distant planets with intelligent creatures such as giant ants, flying lizards, monster spiders, winged newts or little green men with aerials sprouting from their heads.

All, again, bore some resemblance to things known to Man, because not even the most active imagination is capable of creating something completely different from the things we have experienced on Earth.

Today—at last—science has the tools with which to determine the real truths.

Automatic spacecraft have already journeyed near Venus and Mars. Men are preparing to land on the Moon. Giant radio and optical telescopes are able to detect objects well towards the fringes of the Universe, and to measure their finite limits.

Today we know enough to be able to define the Moon and planets with confidence, and to construct models which are based on fact or sound conjecture rather than fancy.

The illustrations in this book, then, are extrapolations from fact—not fiction. They have been built up as a result of scientific research, in much the same way as it is possible to reconstruct prehistoric animals, plants and landscapes to give an accurate picture of ancient times. No doubt discoveries in the future will necessitate that corrections be made to them: but I believe these will be minor and supplement rather than change them in essence.

So, at this point, we might leave our 7,926-mile-wide planet—where, because west to east rotation makes everything else in the sky appear to be going the other way—it is tempting to believe that we are at the hub of the Universe—and take a close look at some of the other members of the Solar System.

It is something which astronauts will one day certainly be able to do, assuming that Man's ingenuity continues to advance at its present pace.

Our first port of call will be the Moon, for that is the body nearest to us and the one which tops the list of priorities for actual space exploration.

In reality, the Moon may well become the springboard to the rest.

13. *The western section of the Moon's Mare Imbrium, with craters Archimedes (right), Autolycus (upper left) and Aristillus (lower left) illuminated by the setting sun. (Photo—Mt Wilson.) See our reconstruction of the foot of the crater Aristillus, Plate 13.*

LIST OF PLATES

1. *The Earth and Moon as they might look from Hermes, a small asteroid which sometimes approaches to within 219,000 miles of the Earth*
2. *The nucleus of a comet approaching Earth*
3. *'Bare, cracked cliffs in the distance, lined by deep abysses' — part of the Moon as it may appear to astronauts*
4. *'Before touch-down... astronauts will undoubtedly draw a great deal of aesthetic satisfaction from a look back at their home planet' — This is how it should look*
5. *A solar eclipse, as seen from the surface of the Moon*
6. *View near the Moon's poles, where the peaks are constantly lit by sunlight, and the valleys immersed in perpetual frost*
7. *The floor of a lunar crater*
8. *The terraced inner wall of a lunar crater*
9. *The Straight Wall on the Moon*
10. *The Moon — Rills near the crater Aridaeus*
11. *The Moon — A close-up of the Hygnius Cleft*
12. *The Lunar Alps*
13. *The Moon's Apennine range, on the north-west edge of the Mare Imbrium*
14. *Rills, as they might look on Mount Aristillus on the Moon*
15. *Part of a lunar sea near the crater Hortensius. The protuberances are domes*
16. *Crater between Copernicus and Eratosthenes*
17. *A lunar crater, with light-coloured rays*
18. *'Hundreds of miles of desolate, burned-out terrain, rocky plains and bare, brightly coloured rocks'...that is Venus*

19. *Venus, the planet no man has seen because of the thick clouds that shroud it*

20. *A dried-out sea on Venus*

21. *Landscape in the tropical region of Venus*

22. *This was how I visualised Venus before America's Mariner spacecraft found temperatures too high to support water on the planet*

23. *Mercury — 'There are large craters, parched deserts and probably a multitude of cliffs...'*

24. *Close-up of Mercury's cliffs with desert in the background*

25. *Mercury, as it might look in the 'Twilight Zone'*

26. *Mars, as it might appear from one of its two satellites — Deimos*

27. *'Old Martian mountains, now severely eroded, whose crumbling cliffs are slowly being blown down into the plains...'*

28. *'Much of Mars is today buried in what looks like dust'*

29. *'The whole planet (Mars) is slowly turning into a gigantic desert'*

30. *Mars — 'The water vapour is hungrily absorbed by the atmosphere'*

31. *Jupiter, as it might look from its satellite Ganymede. The dark stripes can be clearly seen*

32. *'The one big vivid spot in Jupiter's southern hemisphere which has given rise to so much speculation'*

33. *'Huge, mushroom-shaped clouds would billow to a tremendous height over Jupiter, in the manner of a hydrogen bomb test on Earth'*

34. *Saturn — The Ringed Planet*

35. *'Saturn's chief claim to fame is its rings — flat, light-reflecting bands which encircle the planet'*

36. *'The most recent view is that Saturn's rings are made up of millions of separate fragments'*

37. *The rings of Saturn, as they might appear from the surface of the planet*

38. *Uranus, as it might look from its satellite Oberon*

39. *Neptune — is it solid like this?*

40. *Pluto is another extremely cold planet*

PLATES

THE MOON

The first journey made by men to the Moon—in a spacecraft boosted by chemical rockets—will take about three days.

It will hardly be a joy-ride, for—apart from the risk of a failure or explosion of the lifting rocket—there are belts of trapped radiation around the Earth to be negotiated, meteors to be missed and the possible eruption of a dangerous solar flare to be taken into account.

The need to conserve weight will restrict food and water, quarters are sure to be cramped, and the astronauts must all the time perform their tasks without the strong and comforting tug of Earth's gravity.

Even when they reach the Moon it is hardly likely to seem a very welcoming place.

But before touch-down—while the spaceship is still circling the Moon in search of its prearranged landing place—they will undoubtedly draw a great deal of aesthetic satisfaction from a look back at their home planet.

Observed from 240,000 miles—the actual distance varies between 221,500 and 252,700 miles—the Earth will appear to be just the same sort of flat disc as the Moon appears to be from *it*.

It will, however, look three times as large (the Moon is actually 0.273 of its diameter).

This assumes, of course, that the spaceship arrives at the Moon at the right time and in the right place to see the Earth as a complete disc. For the planet goes through 'phases' just as the Moon does and sometimes appears as a crescent and sometimes as half an orb when viewed from space.

When it is full it illuminates parts of the Moon with fairly strong reflected sunlight—more intense than moonlight appears on Earth. This explains why we can sometimes see some of the Moon, which is in shadow, glowing weakly none the less—a phenomenon aptly called 'earthshine'.

The best time to observe it is after sunset in the spring when the Moon rises as a thin crescent in our sky.

Some of this 'earthshine' may filter in through the spaceship's windows; but it would only be noticeable to the crew if they were out of the direct glare of the Sun.

PEŠEK

1. The Earth and Moon as they might look from Hermes, a small asteroid which sometimes approaches to within 219,000 miles of the Earth

Even if they were able to look back when the Earth was shining as a mere crescent they would still be able to make out the complete circular outline of the planet, for a thin border of light would mark the rim.

This glowing line is explained by the fact that our planet's atmosphere bends the Sun's rays, so that some of them reach even the part that is in shadow.

A beautiful sight! Each of the spacemen who have so far orbited the Earth has remarked upon the ethereal loveliness of the 'halo'.

The Moon, by contrast, will have no such border, for it lacks a dense atmosphere to bend the Sun's rays.

The rest of space, as seen from the spaceship, will look very empty indeed. It has no 'up' or 'down' to it. No matter where the eye roams there is only bottomless black space, filled with stars, to meet it. Astronauts report that they have experienced no comparable sensation on Earth, not even when flying 'blind' through clouds.

Although space itself is dark, the Sun—when viewed from outside the filtering layers of our atmosphere—is brilliant: a white hot ball, surrounded by a glowing corona. Although it is hard to look directly at the Sun for more than a few seconds on Earth, it will be impossible to look at it in space. The penalty for attempting to do so is certain blindness.

There are two reasons for this. Our eyes are adapted to looking at the Sun through a filter—our air. This masks about 30 per cent of its radiation. Without this filter the Sun's intense infra-red rays could easily destroy the retina of an eye, causing a condition known as helioscotoma or coagulative necrosis.

The other reason is that by comparison with the fireball, the surrounding heavens look a particularly deep, inky-black when seen from a spaceship. The pupils of the crew's eyes, therefore, widen in adjustment to this; and if they suddenly focus on to the white disc of light they cannot contract as rapidly as they do on Earth. The result is that more radiation will penetrate to the retinas.

Something of the effect can be experienced by looking at a lit electric bulb. If daylight surrounds the bulb it is easy to stare

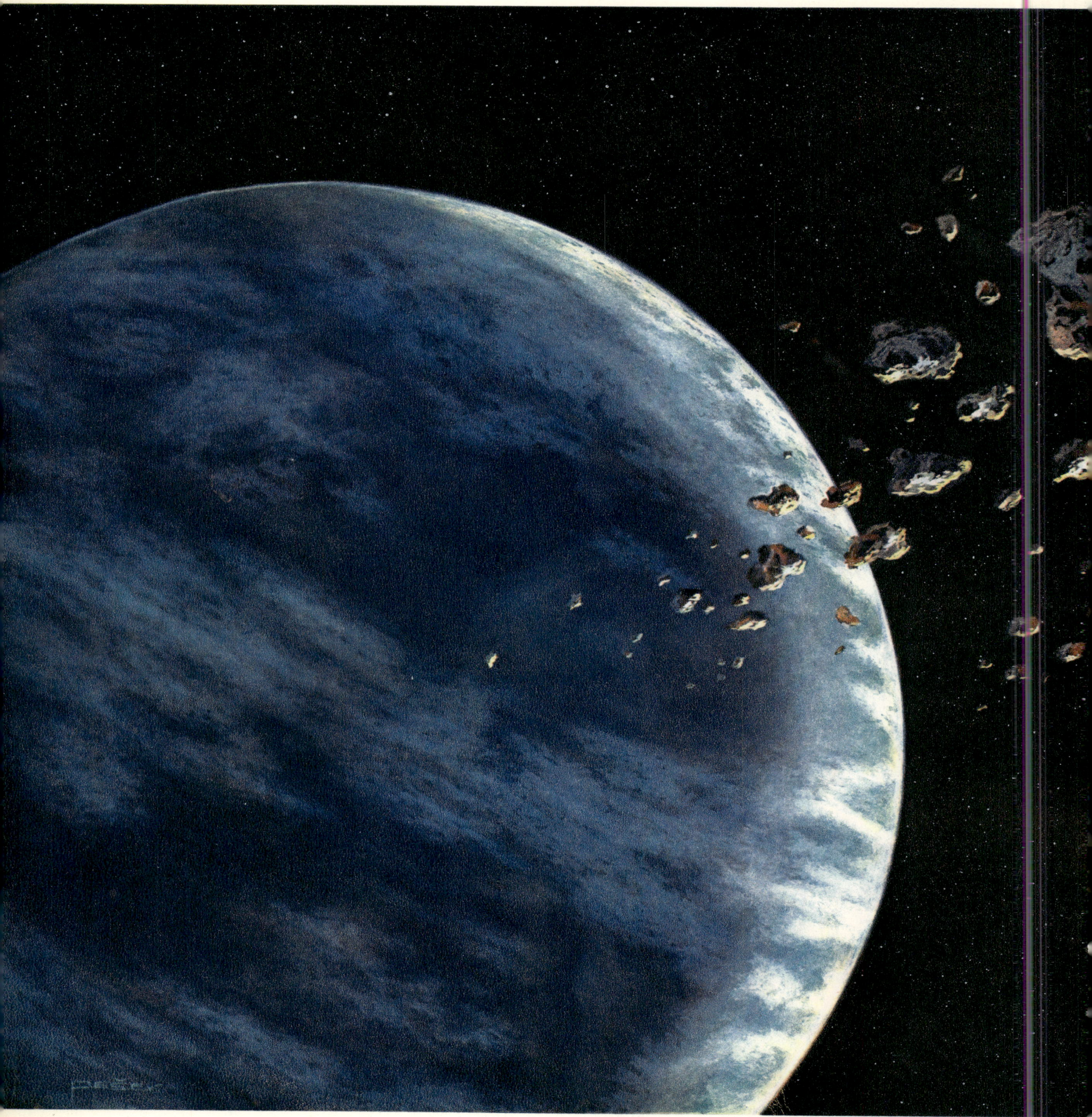

2. *The nucleus of a comet approaching Earth*

at it. But if the room is pitch black when the light is switched on the eye retinas react painfully.

The effect is one which has concerned space medicine experts greatly. For that reason, special sun-glasses—which automatically adjust themselves to changes in the intensity of light—have been developed for astronauts.

Now back to the Moon.

The space near it is far from being empty. The spaceship all the time runs the risk of collision with a meteor or asteroid, and will certainly feel the impact of dust particles called micrometeors. It will also meet invisible atoms, mainly of hydrogen.

For this reason, spaceships are designed with several 'skins', so that if one is punctured another is there to seal off the precious air inside.

The problem of where the ship is to land is likely to have been settled long before take-off from Earth after careful analysis of photographs taken by automatic as well as manned spacecraft in orbit close to the Moon's surface.

The Moon certainly has a hard crust: but this is believed to be covered by a layer of dust, ash or the cinders of some porous mineral like lava or pumice.

How thick this covering is, or how much it varies from spot to spot, no-one yet knows. Some astronomers have suggested that the so-called *maria* or seas which can be seen so clearly on the Moon's face may in fact be areas of very deep dust and that it would be prudent of spaceships to keep clear of these.

Experiments carried out in America with rocket nozzles blasting dust layers indicate that dust would constitute a hazard if it were several feet deep.

The Moon is also sprinkled, for certain, with rock fragments ranging from large boulders to small stones. These are the by-products of collisions with meteors and the collapse of cliffs, and could well spoil a landing.

In the light of present knowledge, the ideal 'moondrome' would seem to be the bottom of one of the thousands of craters which pit the lunar surface.

There are some 30,000 of these on the side of the Moon nearest to us, ranging from ones measuring as much as 190 miles across

3. 'Bare, cracked cliffs in the distance, lined by deep abysses' —
part of the Moon as it may appear to astronauts >

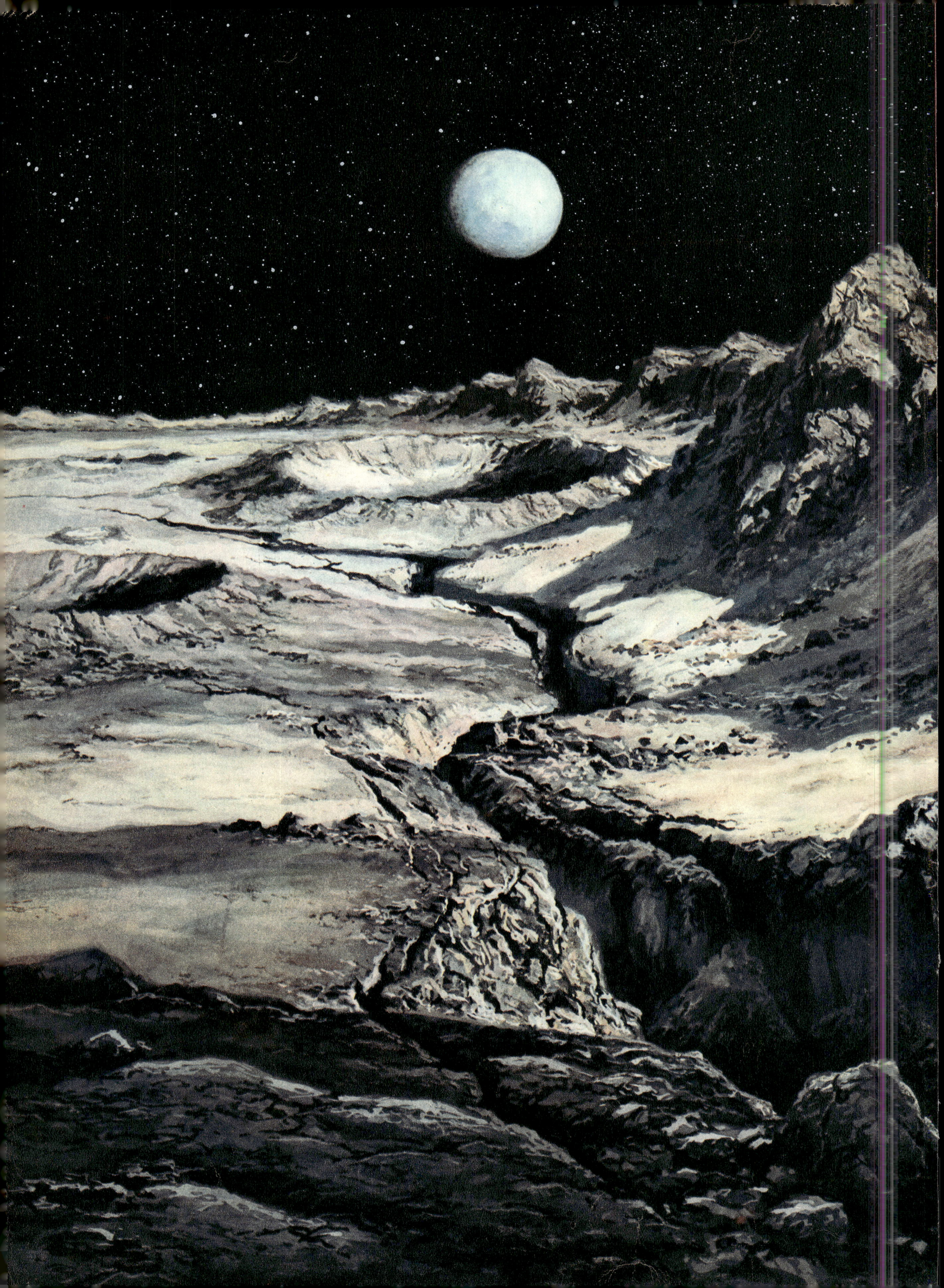

down to some with diameters of only a few hundred yards, which are barely visible from Earth.

These craters look very different from the majority of volcanic craters on the Earth. They appear more like shallow, saucer-like depressions in the Moon's surface, surmounted by low walls.

Volcanic craters are usually located high on conical hills, and the only counterparts to the 'saucers' on the Moon that we know are the steep-walled depressions like Crater Lake in Oregon, U.S.A. and some of the Hawaiian volcanoes.

One of the prime purposes in sending men to the Moon is to determine how these craters got there. Are they the result of the upper layers of the Moon deforming? Are they explosive volcanoes? Could some of them have been formed by the impact of meteors?

We have not long to wait to find out.

It would be an extraordinary coincidence if *all* of them were the result of meteor collisions. But without an atmosphere to slow them down, meteors would certainly make a much more pronounced impression and explode more violently on the Moon than on Earth.

The strongest arguments against a meteoric cause are some peculiarities in the craters themselves. They have terraced inner slopes and other characteristics which lead us to believe that they were probably the result of the Moon's crust collapsing rather than of externally-caused explosions.

The only recent evidence to support the idea that the craters might be volcanic came in 1958 when a Russian astronomer, N. Kosirev, observed what looked like a cloud of gas coming from a point close to the central mound of a crater called Alphonsus.

The event—call it explosion or eruption if you like—lasted about fifteen minutes. Afterwards a reddish-grey spot remained which was studied by several astronomers.

At the time, analysis of the light coming from the gas cloud indicated the presence of carbon.

What caused the eruption? Are there volcanoes on the Moon still active enough to spew out gas or lava? Or do gases, trapped in the Moon's interior, occasionally seep out through cracks

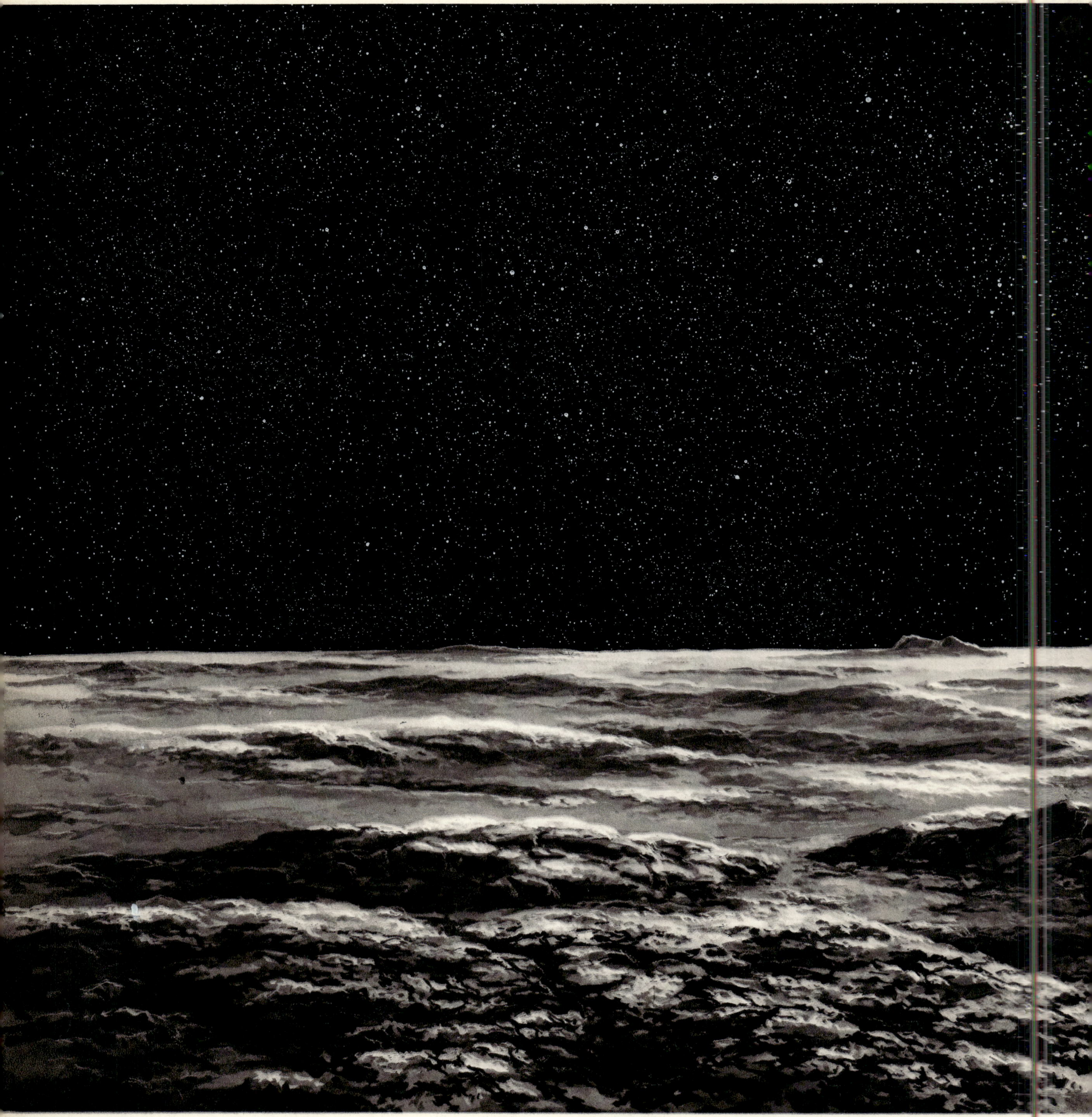

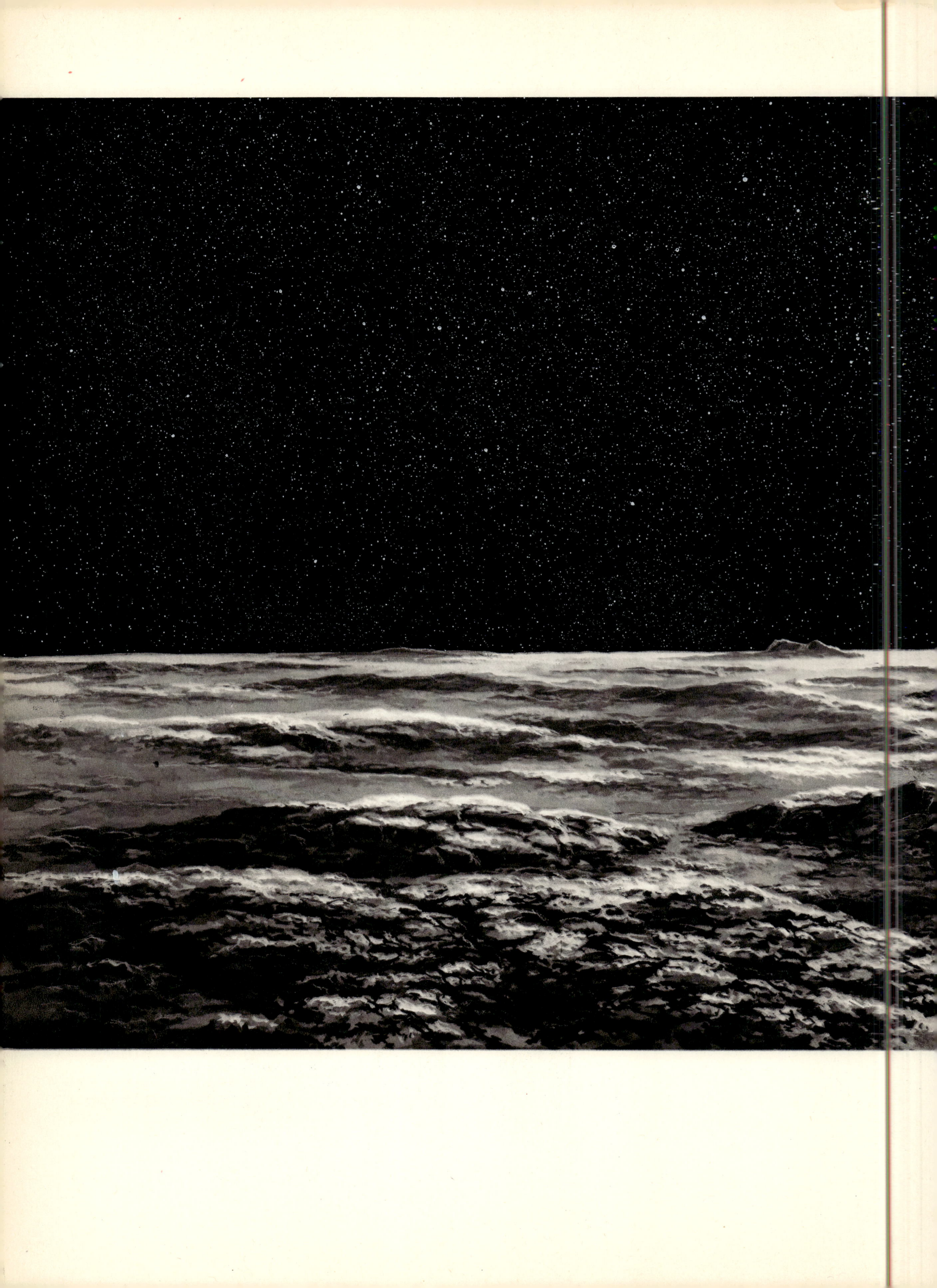

4. '*Before touch-down... astronauts will undoubtedly draw a great deal of aesthetic satisfaction from a look back at their home planet*' — *This is how it should look*

which may suddenly appear as a result of the Moon's crust distorting?

A possible explanation is that fierce chemical reactions may take place not very far below the surface. This implies the presence of an abundance of free elements and active molecules of gas in the Moon's crust—held there because they are frozen.

The Sun's radiation—X-rays, cosmic rays and so on—then strikes a particular spot, triggering a violent reaction underground. The surface suddenly erupts and gas is discharged.

If this is so—if the necessary ingredients *are* frozen into the Moon—then the top layer must be a very poor conductor of heat. For at times the outside temperature climbs very high indeed.

A large number of scientists think that the Moon has retained its original appearance ever since its surface solidified. Without wind or rain to erode it, this is possible. These experts claim that at the same time as the crust hardened there was considerable volcanic activity, plus a gradual, or at times explosive escape of gas from the interior.

They liken the process to that which takes place when molten quartz solidifies. For when quartz cools, crater-like formations similar to those on the Moon result.

If this is the true origin of the lunar 'pock-marks', then the Earth's primary crust probably once looked the same. Our atmosphere, though, gradually smoothed it out.

The craters are probably the most tantalising of all the Moon's riddles and may contain the key to the origin of the Earth's big satellite.

At one time it was thought that the Moon was originally part of the molten Earth, but was torn out—from where the Pacific Ocean now lies—by the pull of the Sun.

Experiments have shown, however, that this hypothesis is most unlikely and modern theory supposes the Moon to have originated in a cold state at the time when the whole Solar System was formed.

Back now to the astronauts circling in their spaceship. The first and following two or three landings will surely be made on the side of the Moon nearest to Earth. Although the Russian space probe, Lunik 3, showed the far side to be remarkably similar

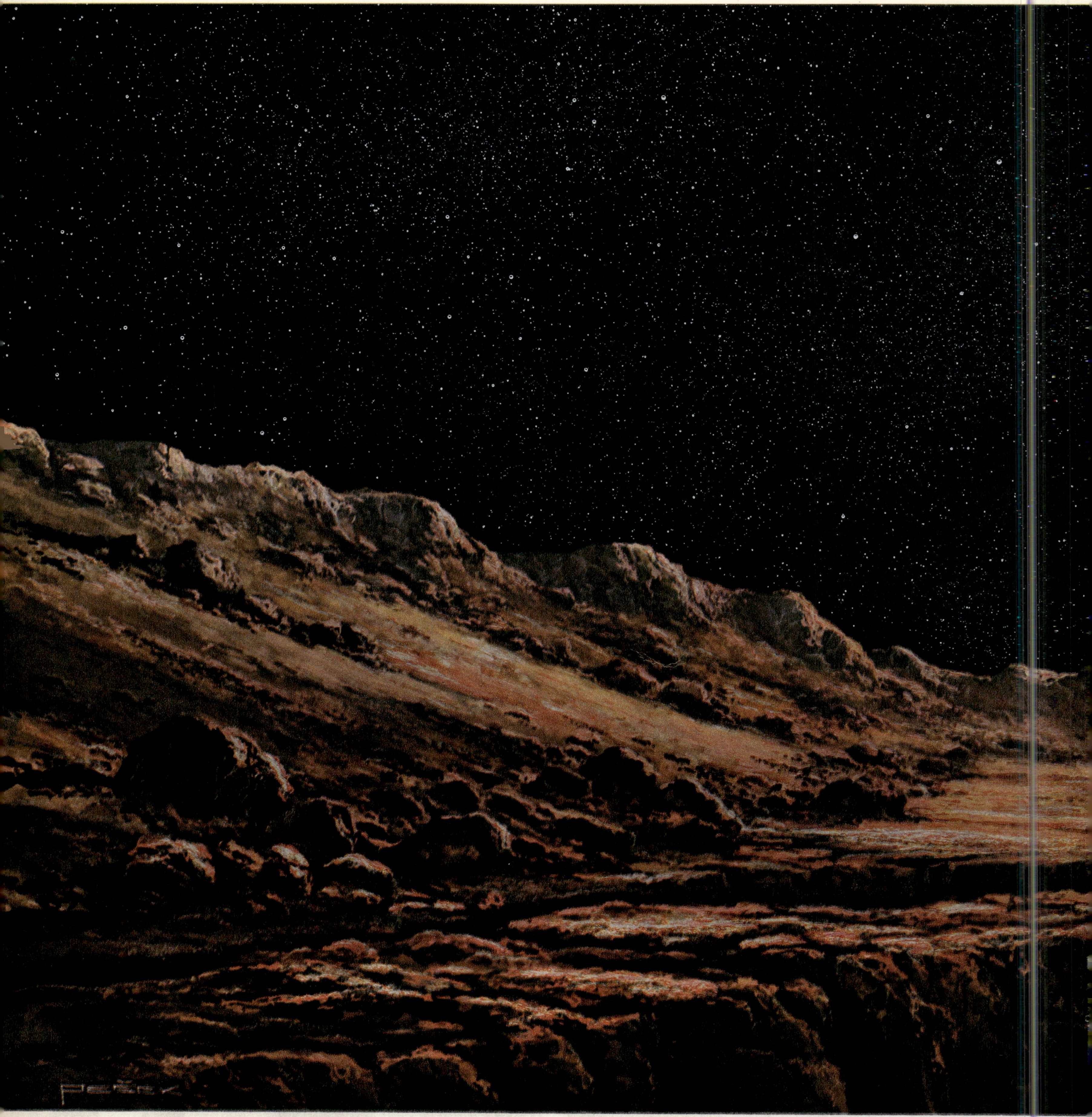

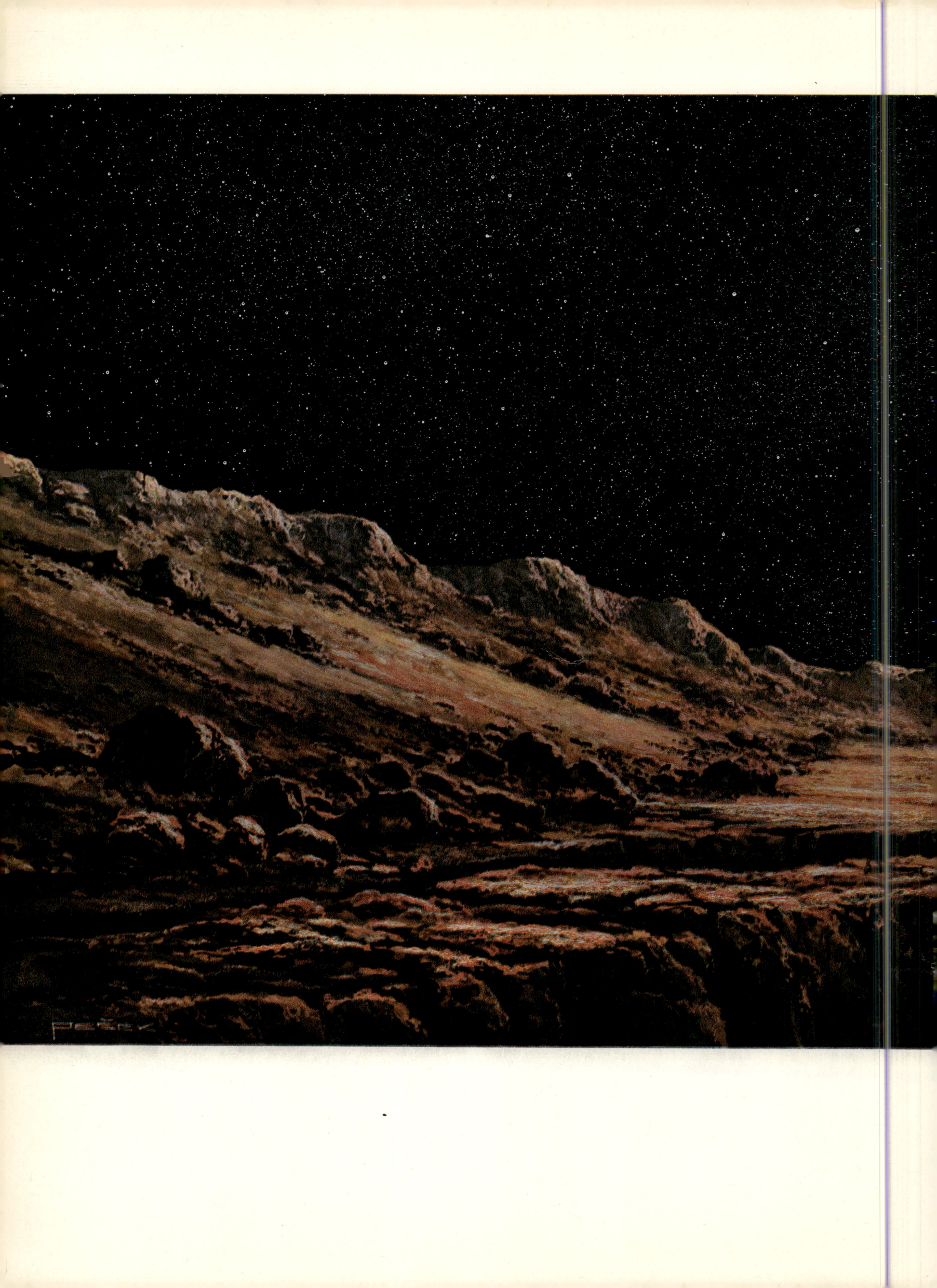

5. *A solar eclipse, as seen from the surface of the Moon*

to the one we can see, the difficulty of maintaining radio contact with home from that side precludes its use.

The actual touchdown will be cushioned by rocket motors squirting out jets of gas.

Picture now what follows. After, presumably, a big sigh of relief, the crew release their exit hatch and prepare to become the first humans to alight on another body in the Solar System.

As they gaze around, they note some striking differences from the Earth they have left.

There is not a sign of refreshing green: instead, a general gloom, with contrasts of black and white. The way the light plays is awe-inspiring. The glare, in places, is fierce, the shadows unusually black by comparison.

Bare, cracked cliffs in the distance, lined by deep abysses; and yet the terrain seems less craggy, less sharply pointed than is usually depicted in science fiction.

This is because the old fictional descriptions of the Moon were based on photographs in which the shadows cast by high ground were very long. Only recently was it realised that *all* these early photographs were taken when the Sun was very low down on the Moon's horizon, thus making everything seem taller and sharper in shadow than it really is.

There certainly *are* mountains, and high ones at that. But they are fewer in number than was once professed.

On the whole the terrain is gently undulating rather than jagged. And behind it all there is a backdrop of absolutely inky sky, spangled with millions of stars. The scene is the same, morning, noon and night, sunrise or sunset, and because there is no air to scatter the light rays the horizon is never anything but black. The absence of atmosphere is responsible for another striking difference between the Moon and its parent planet. For there is nothing to distort the landscape. As far as the eye can see, everything is sharp and clear.

It is difficult, though, to estimate distance without familiar terrestrial yardsticks such as buildings, trees or bushes. Cliffs appear to be anything between a few hundreds of yards away to several miles.

There are just two aids to distance-judging on the Moon—the

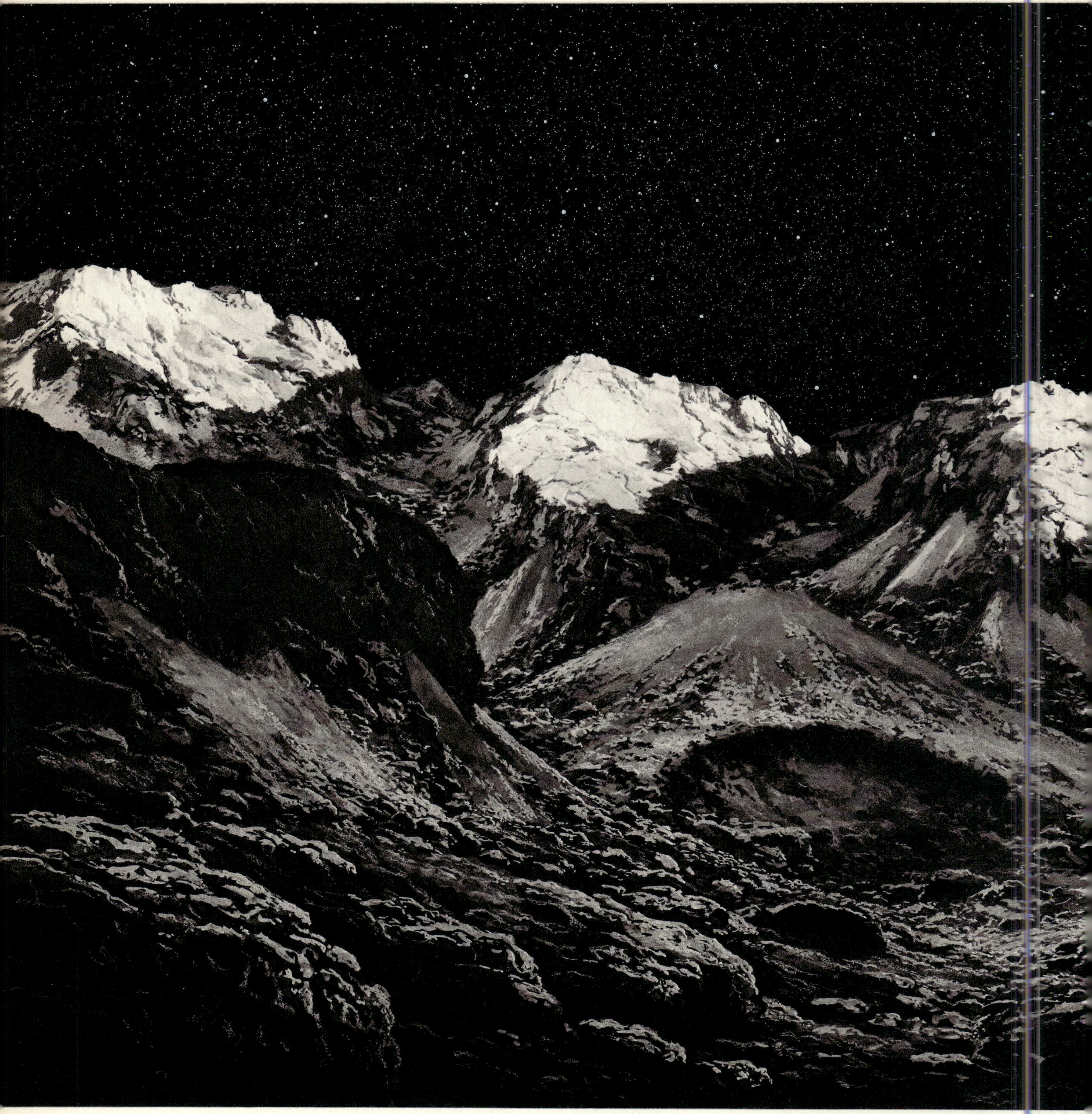

6. *View near the Moon's poles, where the peaks are constantly lit by sunlight, and the valleys immersed in perpetual frost*

displacement of objects caused by the observer moving, and the fact that, on flat ground, the limit of the horizon is about 1½ miles.

On Earth we can see double that distance: but the Moon is smaller, therefore its surface is more curved.

As the astronauts move away from their ship—the dust on the surface of one of the big craters is unlikely to be more than an inch or two deep—they undergo an extraordinary sensation. They bound. A natural step takes them several feet across the ground, and they experience the thrill of being able to take gigantic strides.

This is because the gravity of the Moon is only a sixth of that on Earth. Physical exertion, therefore, produces dramatic results.

If the astronauts were to kick a boulder it could bounce along like a rubber ball.

It would, however, bounce silently—another remarkable difference between Moon and Earth. To carry sound you need air, or a solid conductor. Around the Moon there is only a vacuum. Even if there were a huge explosion on the surface, visitors would hear nothing of it and feel nothing of its shock wave. The only evidence might be a slight tremor of the ground underfoot.

An eerie place, indeed!

Absence of an atmosphere means that all astronauts who move about the face of the Moon will have to take their own little 'worlds of air' with them as they go. Their spacesuits must be tough and durable, for a tear on a jagged edge of rock or a puncture would be followed by a horrible event known as explosive decompression.

If this should occur all the gas inside the suit rushes out into the vacuum of space and the blood boils immediately.

But the vacuum conditions on the Moon have one big advantage—they make star-gazing considerably easier. Stars only appear to twinkle when viewed from the Earth because their light rays are broken up in our atmosphere. From the Moon they will seem steady and still.

Stars which might pass out of the field of vision of a fixed telescope on Earth in 2 minutes, would remain in view for 54 minutes on the Moon. This is because it rotates much more slowly.

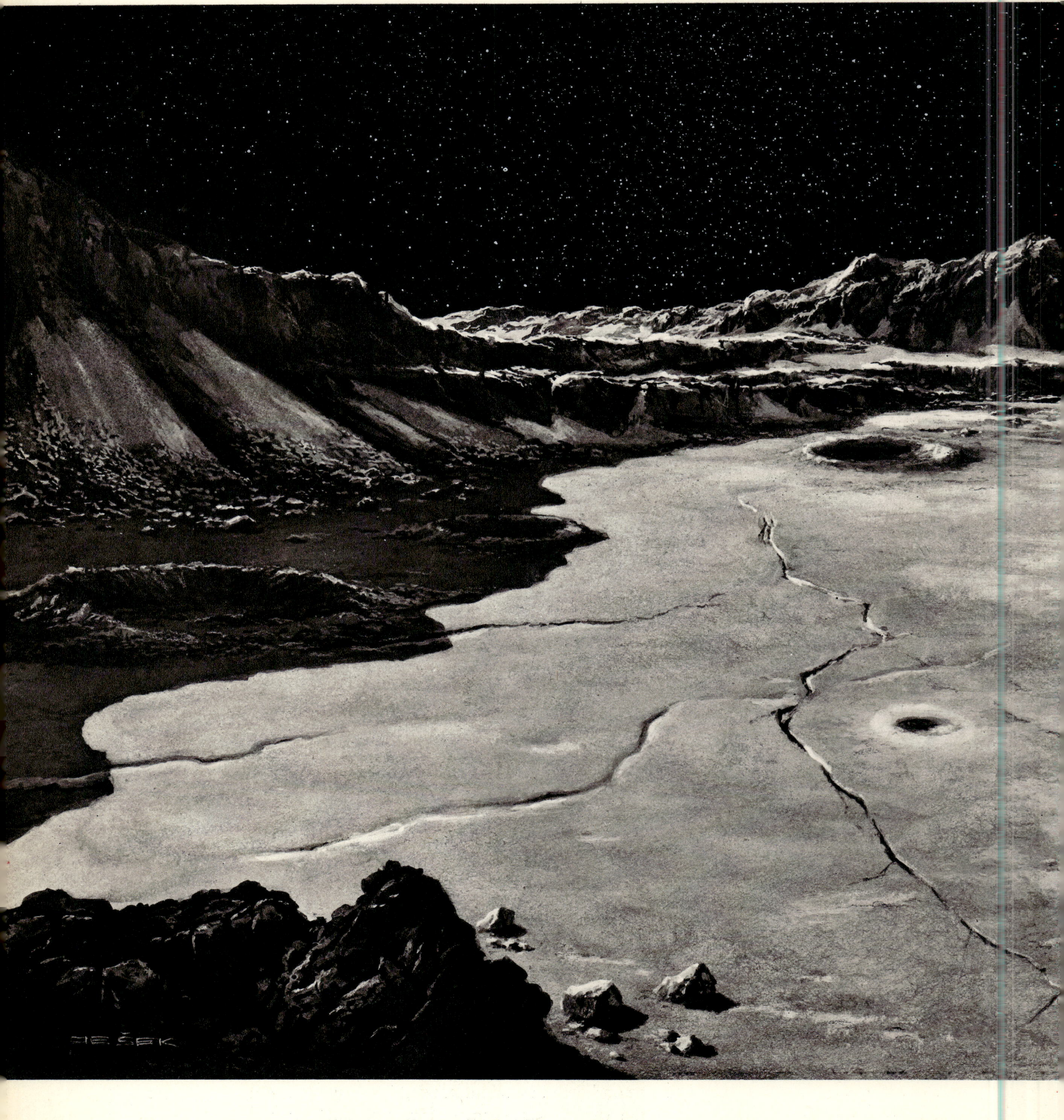
HEŠEK

7. *The floor of a lunar crater*

For this reason many astronomers look forward to the day when observatories can be erected on the Moon. Even during the daytime there the stars are visible.

'Daytime' or 'a night' on the Moon are quite different from our understanding of these things on Earth. They last considerably longer.

By 'daytime', of course, we mean the time during which the Sun is above the horizon. This, in the Moon's case, is a little more than half a *sidereal month*: and a sidereal month is the period of time it takes the Moon to revolve around the Earth once—27 days 7 hours 43 minutes and 11½ seconds on average.

So for a little more than one of our Earth fortnights our astronauts will feel the Sun burning down on them: then will follow a fortnight of night.

During the whole period, the stars they see will appear to travel completely round the Moon. In reality it will be them, on the Moon, rotating—not the stars.

This slow rotation of the Moon exactly matches the time of its journey around our planet, so that to us the Moon always presents the same face. That is why pictures radioed back by Russia's Lunik 3 excited so much interest—because they showed a side of the Moon never before seen by Man.

But the lunar orbit is not without blemishes. It wavers. From time to time it appears to nod at the Earth, and also shake from side to side like a head saying no. This movement is called *libration*.

When it occurs, it enables us to see a little more of the lunar surface than usual. In fact 41 per cent is always visible, 41 per cent is never visible and 18 per cent sometimes is. By the same token astronauts on the Moon during a libration will observe that the Earth does not remain a 'fixed' object in *their* sky; and just as we on Earth see a 'new Moon' or a 'full Moon' or a Moon 'in the last quarter' so the outline of the home planet to *their* eyes will vary from a full disc to a crescent, according to whereabouts on the Moon they are standing and how far the sidereal month has advanced.

It gets very hot on the Moon during the day (i.e. 14 Earth days) and very cold at night. At noon the temperature is estimated

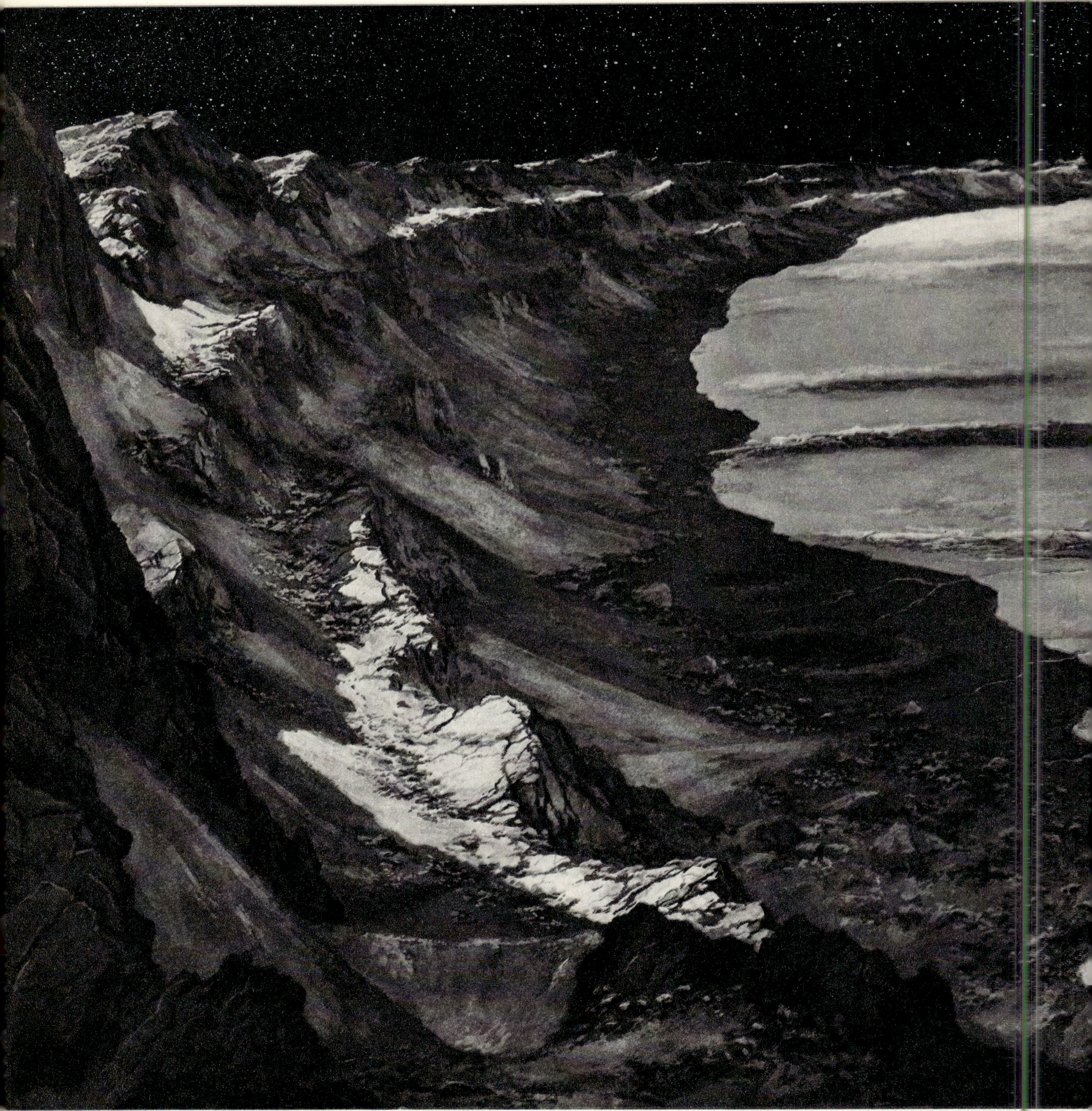

8. *The terraced inner wall of a lunar crater*

to reach 110 degrees Centigrade (230 degrees Fahrenheit), dropping to minus 170 degrees Centigrade (minus 270 degrees Fahrenheit) or even colder at night. This, once again, is due to the fact that there is nothing in the environment to retain the Sun's heat, and no oceans or air to diminish the temperature differences. As soon as the Sun sets, the heat drops away very rapidly, reaching its lowest just before sunrise.

Maximum temperature is only reached in places directly illuminated by the Sun: in shadowed regions—even on the daylight side on the Moon—it stays below freezing.

An interesting phenomenon is the extremely rapid temperature drop observed during an eclipse—i.e. when the Earth comes between the Moon and Sun, casting a shadow on the lunar crust. Just before the eclipse the ground temperature is 70 degrees Centigrade (160 degrees Fahrenheit). As soon as the shadow appears it falls off sharply, reaching minus 50 degrees Centigrade (minus 68 degrees Fahrenheit) in less than an hour.

We conclude from this that the surface of the Moon is a very good insulator—an argument against the theory that chemical reactions under it may be triggered locally by bursts of solar radiation.

Such violent temperature fluctuations—as much as 280 degrees Centigrade (500 degrees Fahrenheit)—pose a special problem for astronauts, and any who plan to spend long periods on the Moon will certainly have to construct or find shelters. Fortunately it takes a lot of Earth days to reach the extremes of day or night, so there is ample time for preparation.

The polar regions of the Moon—its 'north and south' if looked at flat on a map—have special interest as far as day or night are concerned.

The tips of high mountains here—or, to be more precise, the small horizontal planes on their pinnacles—are almost constantly lit by sunlight. They have fairly acceptable temperatures, therefore. But the valleys directly below, by contrast, are immersed in eternal frost and never see sunshine.

The same variations can be observed to a lesser degree all over the Moon. Mountain tops, in general, receive the light of the Sun several hours before the plains and valleys do. Valleys running

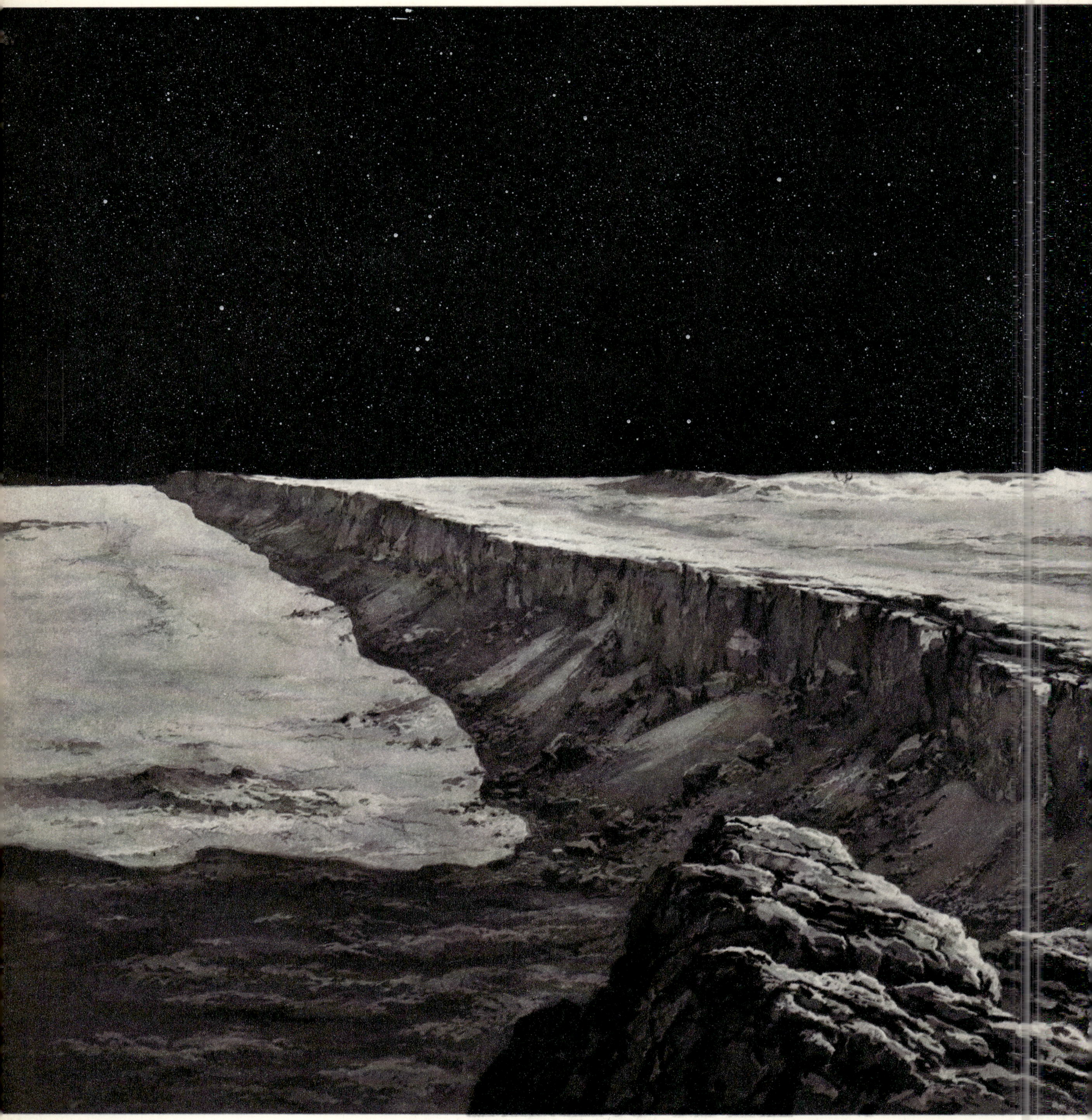

9. *The Straight Wall on the Moon*

from north to south, and which are closed to the south by mountains, rarely see sunlight at all. Such perpetual gloom is not found in valleys of this kind on Earth because our air and daylit sky reflect and disperse the light. But on the Moon all they get is a small reflection from surrounding cliffs which happen to be in the sunshine, and this adds up to a very poor illumination indeed.

Nor is the immobile calm of the Moon's black sky likely to be enlivened by an aurora or 'display of lights'.

Auroras are caused by minute particles of radiation from the Sun striking dilute gases in the upper layers of atmosphere and making them luminous, but the absence of a lunar atmosphere again rules this out.

A colourless place the Moon, then. Nothing but shades of black and white.

The intense bombardment of its surface by rays of sunlight during the day, combined with the rapid cooling that takes place during the long night, undoubtedly takes a toll of the mountains and rocky plains.

Although far too slowly to be noticeable to the astronauts, these surface features are constantly changing—disintegrating into a fine dust scree and sand which piles up at the foot of the steeper mountain slopes. This is not solely due to the effects of heat and cold, but also to the incessant attack of X-rays, ultraviolet rays and radioactive particles from the Sun.

They beat down unhindered by any air layers.

Primary cosmic radiation is the most destructive, for it penetrates four to eight inches into stony ground, breaking up atoms and causing the whole crystalline structure of minerals to change. This eventually leads to complete disintegration of rock or boulder.

Millions of tiny specks of meteor dust rain down as well.

Every so often the ultra-violet rays produce a strange effect on the Moon, making it—when viewed from Earth—seem luminous.

This is due to minerals on the lunar crust absorbing radiation and re-radiating it in the form of light. The process goes on all the time, but the luminescence is only visible when there is no sunlight to drown it—i.e. when the Earth is directly between Moon and Sun, blocking off most of the light.

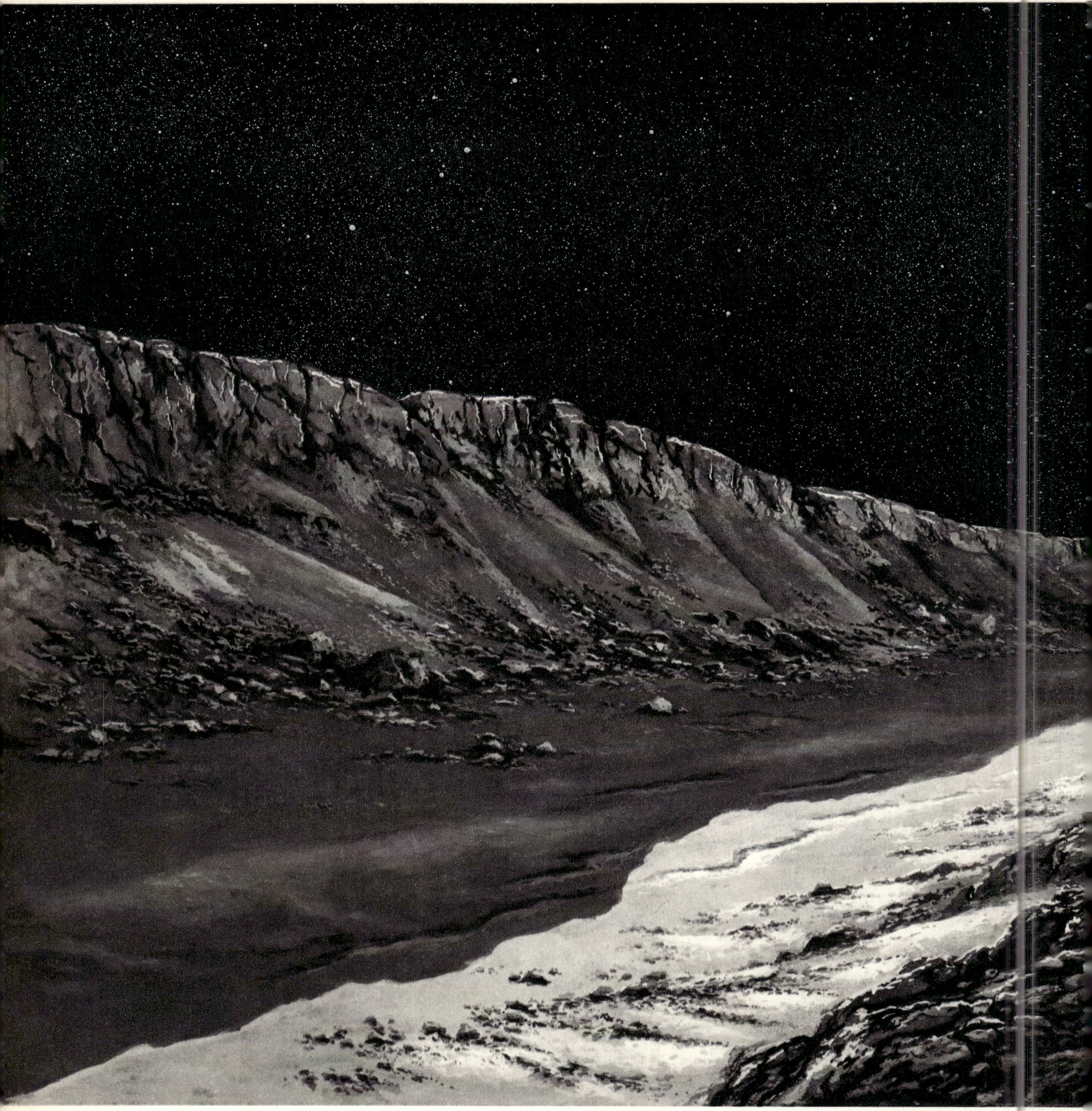

10. *The Moon — Rills near the crater Aridaeus*

We have said, again and again, that the Moon has no atmosphere. For all practical purposes this is so. But the tiny, electrically-charged particles released from minerals under bombardment by the Sun's rays in fact create a volatile 'atmosphere'. Its density is only about one ten thousand millionth of the Earth's atmosphere, that means that it is more refined than is the most perfect vacuum that Man can create.

It is possible that this 'atmosphere'—it sometimes produces a thin, local haze—also contains gases that have escaped from the Moon's interior. But it stretches upwards for some 60 miles.

As far as the astronauts are concerned, however, it might as well not exist.

Earth air, and only Earth air, will help them.

One of their prime missions will undoubtedly be to bring back samples of rock from different parts of the Moon for analysis. They may have to roam quite a long way to get a variety. At least two types of rock are thought to exist there.

One looks like grey granite and could be volcanic in origin. This is believed to lie in the Moon's irregularly shaped 'continents'—the light-coloured patches we can see through telescopes.

The other is a darker substance, probably basalt or gabbro, and this is reckoned to form the basis of the *maria* or 'seas'.

'Seas' are huge, circular sunken basins in which lava appears to have bubbled up and spread.

To resolve such questions as 'How was the Moon formed?' or 'Is there any evidence that its crust once broke apart, sank and shifted?' the astronauts can head for a number of regions of special interest.

One of these is the Mare Imbrium—the Sea of Showers—which lies in the south-east quarter of the Moon, and which is dominated by towering mountains.

On the south-western edge of this 'sea' there is an unusual mountain formation which looks like a long level wall. It can be seen through even a weak telescope from the Earth. Astronomers call it the Straight Wall.

The whole formation is $64\tfrac{1}{2}$ miles long and culminates, at its northern end, in a crater some $3\tfrac{1}{2}$ miles across.

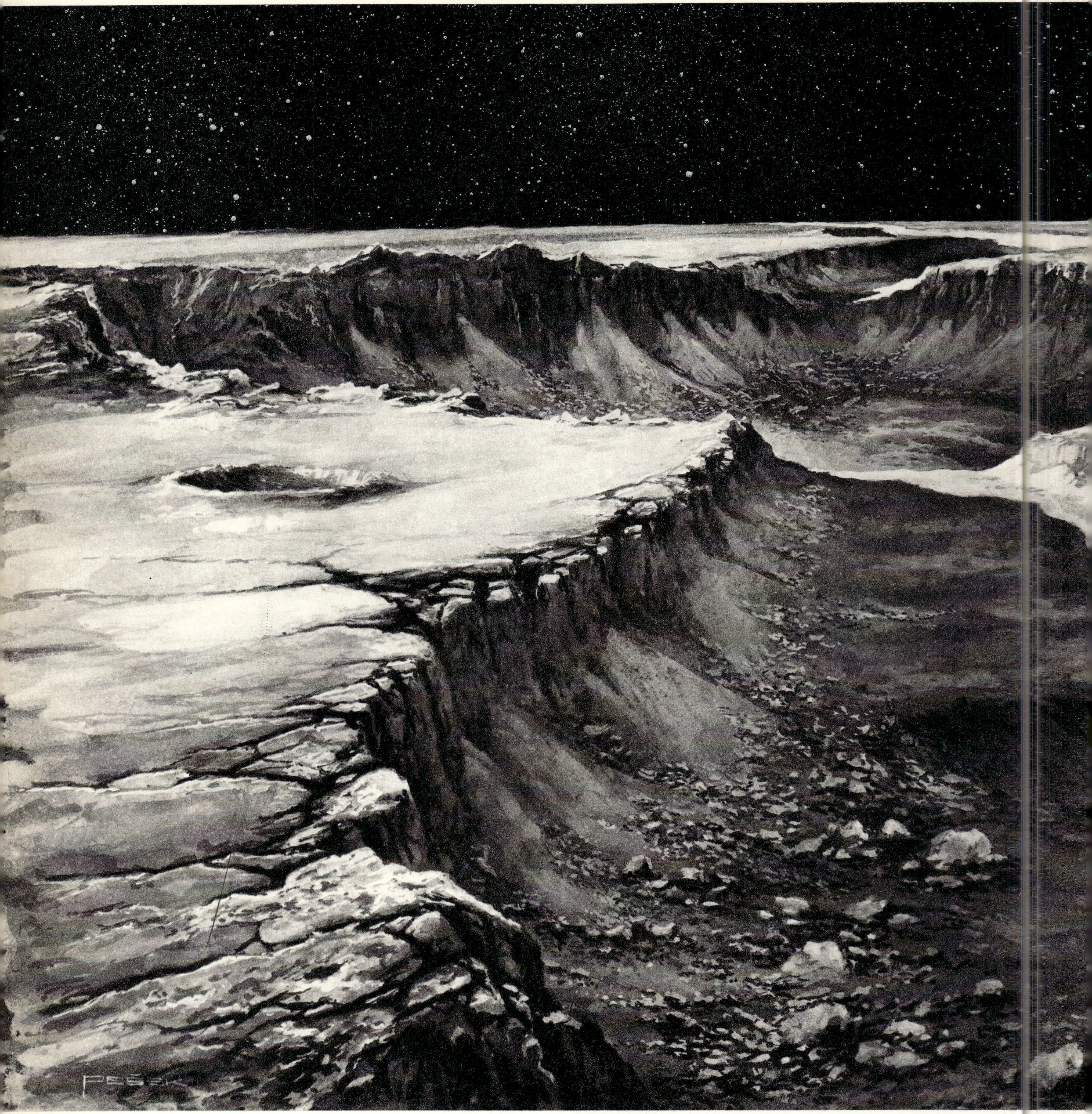
PEŠEK

11. The Moon — *A close-up of the Hygnius Cleft*

In the olden days, Moon watchers were convinced that this wall was artificially constructed—built by intelligent beings. But closer inspection suggests that it is a natural freak—the only one of its kind on the Moon.

It would seem to be a gigantic crack in the Moon's crust, on one side of which the ground has sunk, due to a fault. The other side has somehow become distorted, giving the appearance of a wall 820 feet high.

We know that some of our own planet's contours were the result of continual stresses on the crust over long periods. So we can presume that the lunar surface underwent stresses and motions which caused it to crack in places and tear into pieces, some of which rose while others sank.

If these deep cracks did occur on the Moon—and they may well still be forming—then we can deduce that they would act as exit ports for molten rock below the surface.

Lava and gas might thus pour out on to the surface of the Moon, giving rise to the kind of spectacle seen by the Soviet astronomer Kosirev in 1958.

In addition to the Straight Wall, there are a number of relatively thin, long cracks—particularly near the centre of the lunar disc—which are known as *clefts*.

One theory holds that they were the result of a top layer of molten lava cracking as it solidified across the Moon's surface millions of years ago. If the astronauts could only get down into one of these clefts they should be able to confirm or deny this.

Perhaps their best bet would be to explore a particularly large cleft called Hygnius which is centrally placed. In places it is over $2^1/_2$ miles wide and many hundreds of feet deep. Along the centre of this vast valley runs an elevated ridge.

From the way it lies parallel, it would seem that it once connected the edges of the cleft together.

Powerful telescopes have shown the Hygnius cleft to link a row of crater-like depressions, and argument has raged over the origin of these. Are they like the chains of volcanoes which lie along the cracks in the Earth's crust, such as the phenomenon known as the Laki Fault in Iceland? Or were they caused by explosions, or perhaps by the sudden outburst of gases?

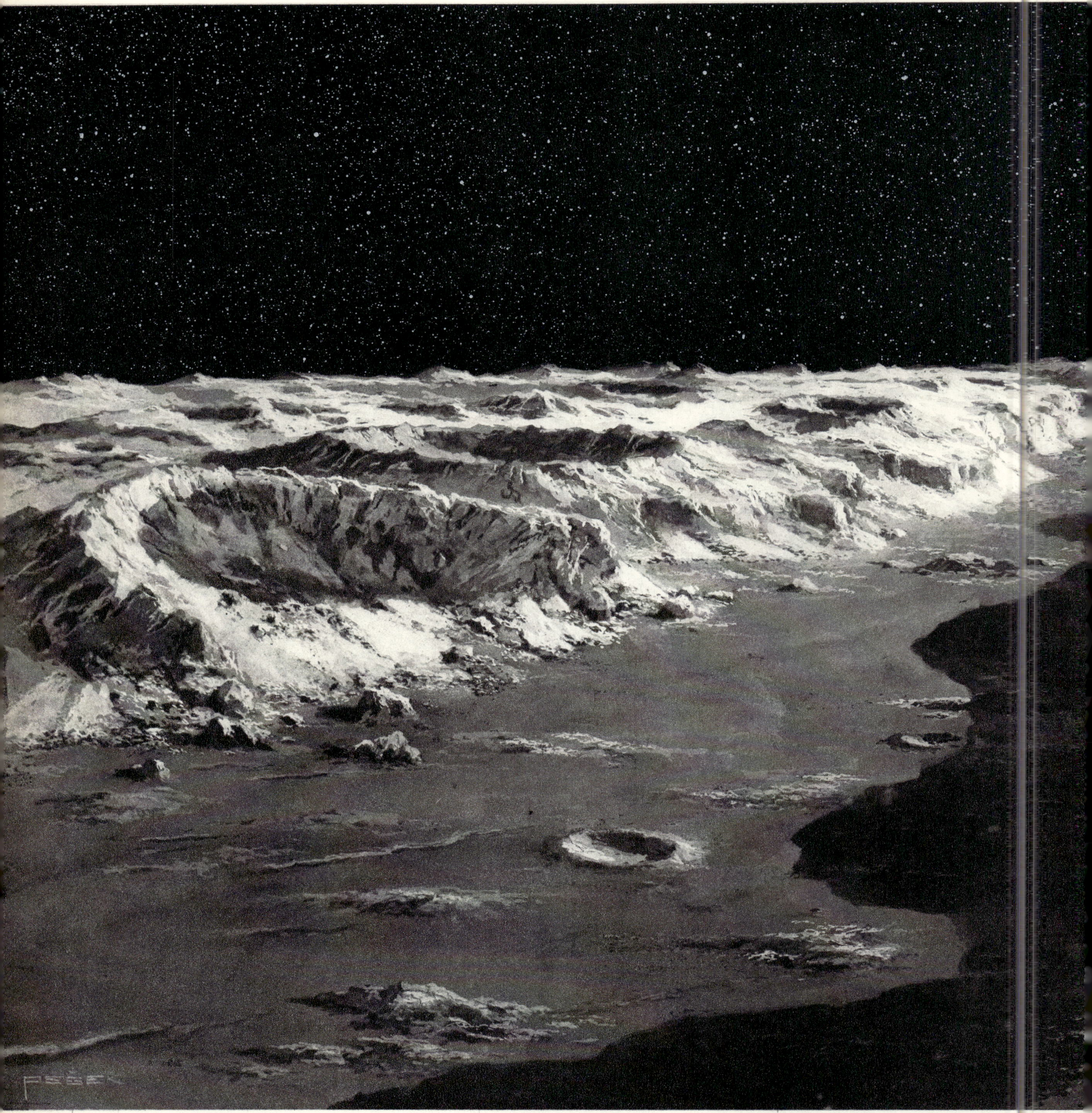

12. *The Lunar Alps*

Certainly one of the round depressions looks as if it were caused by an explosion. And explosive volcanoes are known to occur on Earth.

The so-called *maars* of Java are a counterpart. These are 'canals' in which there has been an eruption of compressed gas. This has given them broad, funnel-shaped extensions. The floor of a *maar* is always lower than the surrounding land.

There is a *maar* in Italy—in the Phlegraean Fields of Naples—called Monte Nuovo. It is more than half a mile in diameter and the surrounding ridge of volcanic rock is 390 feet high.

In the Eifel mountains of Germany, in the Rhineland, there is a larger *maar* which has filled with water and is now called Laach Lake.

It is possible, in my opinion, that such explosive volcanic craters exist on the Moon.

If you observe the Hygnius Cleft from Earth when the Moon is full, it looks like a thin thread of light-coloured wool lying against a dark background. Some scientists attribute this light border to the effects of gas bursts.

The rim is formed, they believe, of minute crystals of various minerals condensed from gases which have escaped through the cleft.

Others say that minerals in the rim have changed their original colour after contact with escaping gases.

One tantalising possibility raised by the clefts is that their depths may contain pockets of trapped carbon dioxide or water vapour. If this were so then conditions might just be favourable enough to support living organisms, although they would have to be extremely hardy to survive.

Only when astronauts have crawled down into the fissures will we know.

Another type of valley lies on the western edge of the Sea of Showers. It ranges from $1^1/_2$ to 8 miles in width and stretches for more than 100 miles between the gaunt peaks of a mountain range named the Lunar Alps.

There are, again, several theories to account for it. One maintains that it was caused by an immense meteorite falling on to the Lunar Alps—not directly from above but from a tangent.

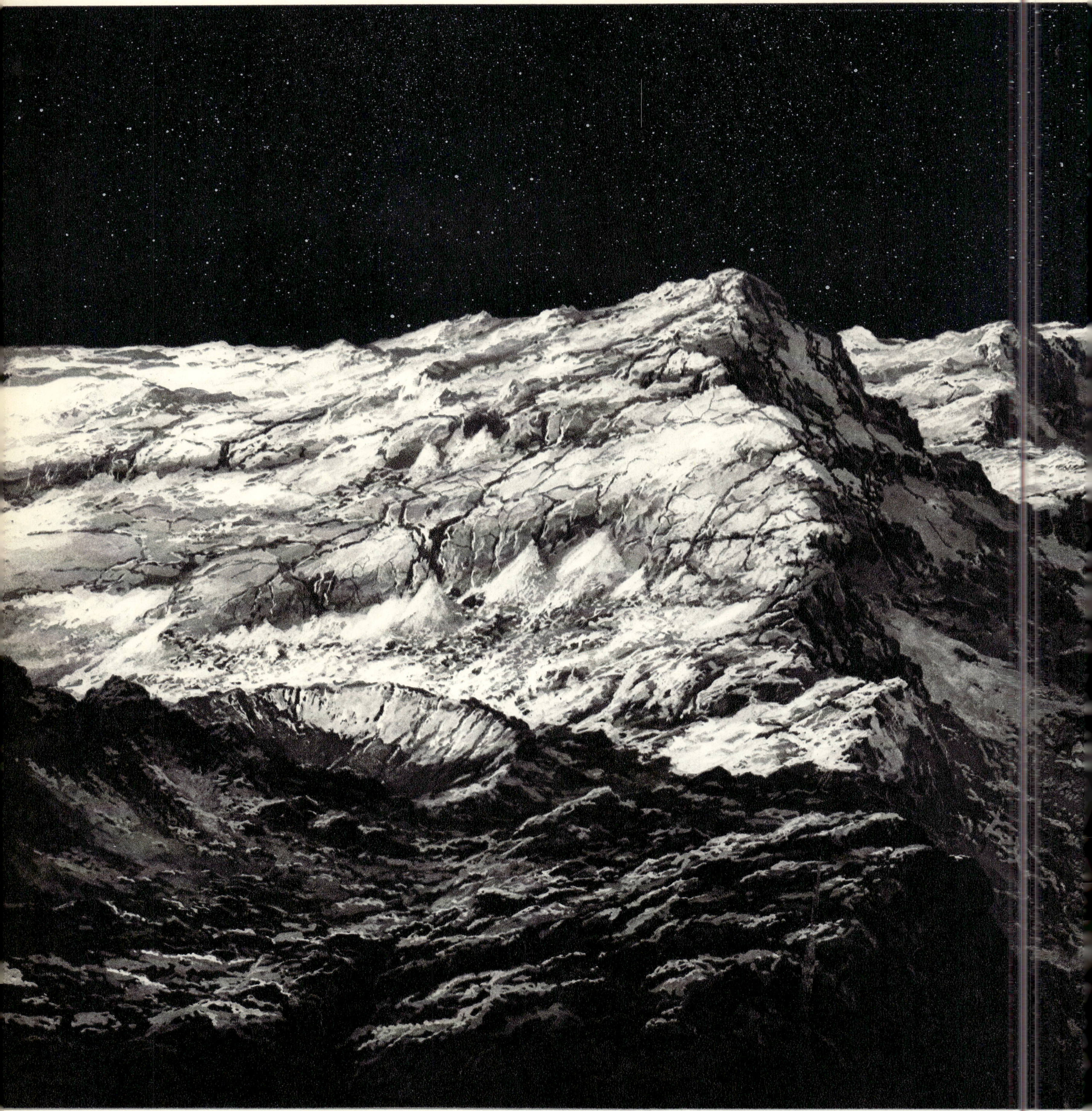

13. *The Moon's Apennine range, on the north-west edge of the Mare Imbrium*

Because the obstacle it struck was solid, the resulting explosion sent shock waves along a straight line to make a furrow rather than a crater.

A more plausible theory, however, suggests that the valley is yet another example of the Moon's crust cracking as a result of motions underneath: that this time the crack split an entire mountain range down the middle. Supporting this is the fact that the two edges of the Alpine valley appear to lock in like a jigsaw, as though they had once been joined together.

Bounding the north-west edge of the Mare Imbrium is another big mountain range—this one called the Apennines. The peaks of this are almost twice as high as the Alps, and from this one concludes that either the 'sea' below them sank or that the Alps sank by comparison.

Evidence that the latter happened comes in the fact that the Alps seem to have been partially flooded with lava from the Mare Imbrium, whereas the Apennines definitely were not.

The highest pinnacle in the Apennines is Mount Huygens, which is about 18,000 feet, and the whole range extends more than 300 miles—the grandest of all on the Moon.

The Sea of Showers, if the first astronauts discover that its surface is not too dusty, might make an easier target for subsequent moonship pilots. It is a vast plain. And somewhere in it—on a spot estimated to lie between three big craters called Archimedes, Autolycus and Aristillus—Russia's Lunik 2 spacecraft impacted on September 13th, 1959.

The Aristillus crater is another of the Moon's mysteries and therefore holds a special appeal for inquisitive astronauts.

Its circular rim is more than 4,500 feet high and the central depression measures 30 miles across. Just outside lies a plateau known as the Marsh of Fogs, or Palus Nebularum.

Around Aristillus's north-eastern wall an unusual pattern of *rills* can be seen, spreading out radially from the centre of the crater like the spokes of a bicycle wheel. These rills, or furrows, are especially noticeable when the Sun strikes them from low down on the lunar horizon.

What are they?

As with so many other things about the Moon there are

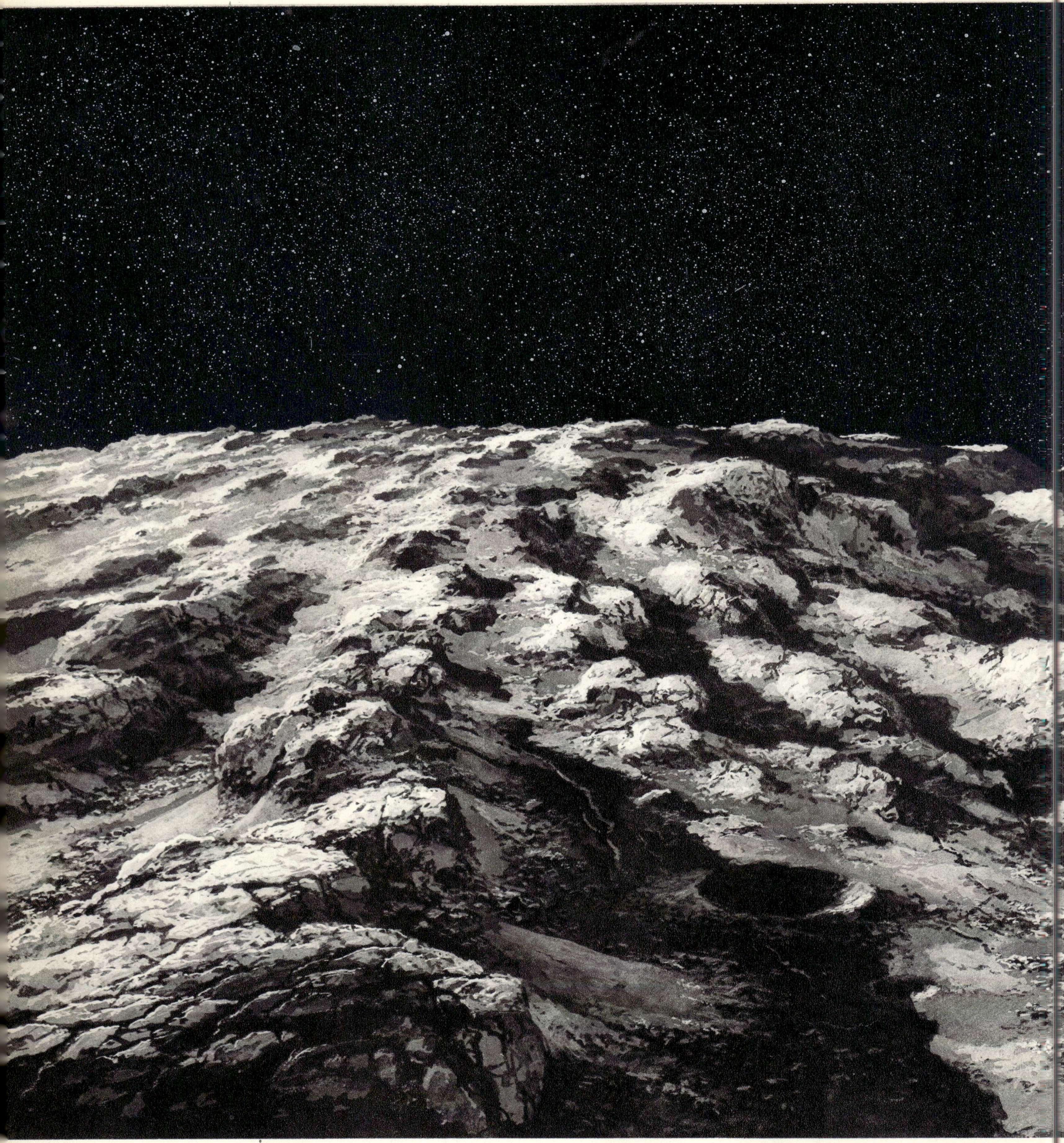

14. Rills, as they might look on Mount Aristillus on the Moon

conflicting theories to explain them. One says they were melted into the crater wall by streams of hot volcanic gas. Another maintains that little rivers of water, condensing from the volcanic vapours that at one time escaped from Aristillus, carved out the furrows.

Neither of these theories seems to me to be correct. It is hard to imagine that volcanic gases could be so hot as to melt solid rock. Nor can one believe that running water could carve such deep, straight rills as the ones in the wall here. Nor are they likely to have come there by accident.

I am left wondering if they might not be the counterpart of some unusual 'rays' discovered many years ago around a crater near Henbury, Australia. This hole in the ground was obviously caused by a large meteorite and the 'rays' run down its walls into the surrounding countryside.

They appear to be veins of hard rock which have withstood erosion by wind and rain much better than their surroundings. The veins are only an inch or two high and are made up from hundreds of small rocks of sandstone which have turned black over the years.

As a result they stand out clearly against the rest of the landscape. Since they appear to be the effects of high pressures set up when the meteorite exploded, it is tempting to believe that Aristillus's rills are the result of similar pressures.

In several other ring formations on the Moon one can see patterns of rays issuing radially from the walls. Sometimes they appear to have their hubs outside the main craters, as though some giant had spattered blobs of pale paint across the lunar crust.

They cast no shadow and appear to have no form. Yet one—in the southern hemisphere of the Moon—stretches over 1,100 miles.

One theory to account for these is that they are light powder or volcanic ash flung out in all directions by explosions. But they may be lines of fine stones and rocks. The interesting thing is that they are only found around craters which are reckoned by many scientists to have been formed comparatively recently. None of the older craters have them.

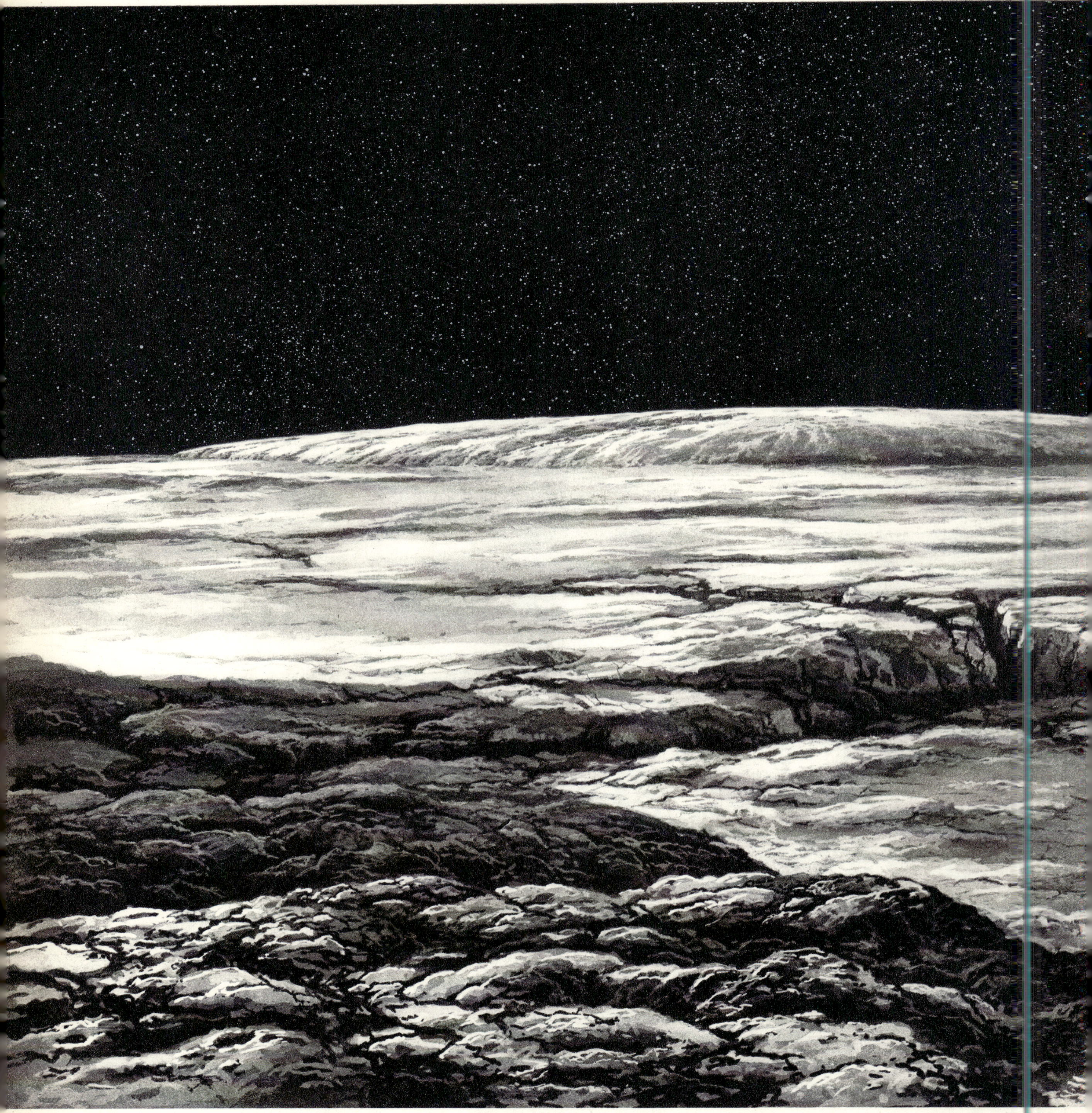

15. *Part of a lunar sea near the crater Hortensius. The protuberances are domes*

The light colour of the rays fits in with the idea that they are fresh streaks of a sub-stratum material which has not yet had time to be darkened by cosmic radiation.

In the middle of the Moon's east flank there lies a large dark plain known as the Ocean of Storms—Oceanus Procellarum.

It, too, is worthy of a visit by astronauts, for it contains examples of another lunar formation—*domes*.

Domes can be several miles in diameter but are never more than a few hundred feet high. They occur only along the edges of the lunar 'seas'—never in the 'continents'. Some have craters on top, others are just plain domes.

Yet again, their origin is unknown. And again, there is a host of theories to account for them.

Some scientists hold that they are bubbles, rising from the lava surface of the 'seas', pushed up by pressure of gases imprisoned below the surface.

Others believe that they correspond to a phenomenon on Earth called a 'shield volcano'—a volcano whose top has not given way. Examples of these can be found in Iceland and the Hawaiian Islands.

It has been suggested that domes are forced up by the pressure of layers of ice in the lunar sub-strata in much the same way that a frozen pipe in a house will bulge.

As we know, the top of the Moon's crust can get hot enough to boil a kettle; but not more than a yard down, the temperature is thought to be 30 degrees Fahrenheit below freezing point.

According to the last theory about the domes, water vapour can come to the surface from the frozen layer through cracks. It gradually accumulates, and this forces the crust to rise—slowly forming a dome. Although some of the water vapour and ice evaporates, says the theory, it is constantly being replaced from below. So the dome keeps rising.

It should be apparent by now—and certainly will be to astronauts on the spot—that the surfaces on the Moon's 'seas' are not nearly as smooth as they seem.

There are mountain peaks, in splendid isolation, clusters of craters, domes, walls and veins which stick up. There are innumerable tiny craters—called *craterlets*—and *craterpits* (these have no raised rim).

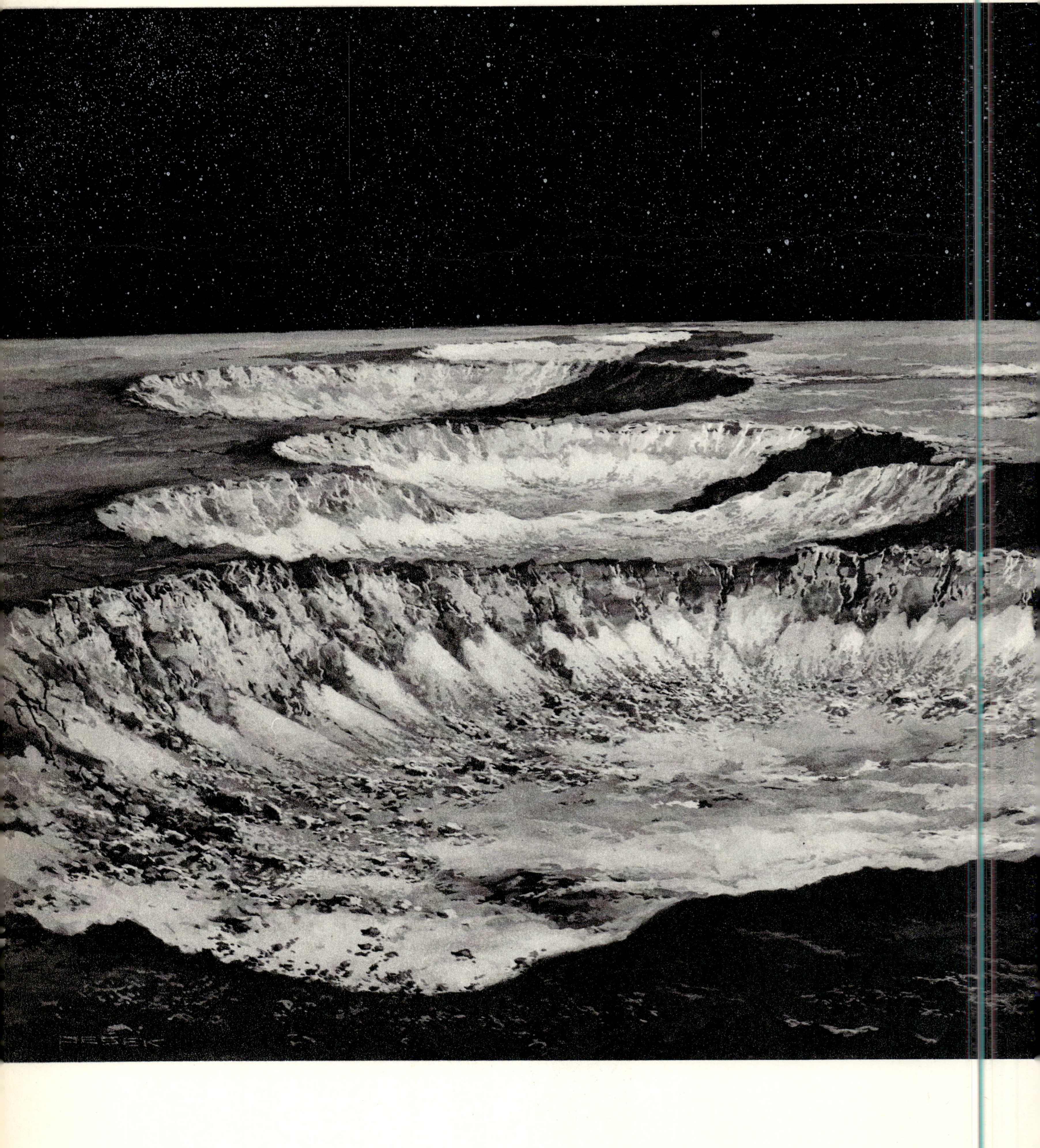
PESEK

16. *Crater between Copernicus and Eratosthenes*

All these cover the 'continents' as well as the 'seas'. They make the Moon an object of extraordinary geological curiosity.

Many scientists believe that the Moon—like the Earth and the other inner planets—is *all the time* at the mercy of powerful, internal processes. These cause the entire sphere to expand or contract, or both.

The circular 'seas' and bigger craters, they say, were all created by this pulsating pressure: and the whole surface of the Moon has either contracted and collapsed, or expanded and cracked—and may still be doing so.

Or so the theory goes.

To explain the craterlets a number of astronomers have claimed that meteorites dug them out. But there is one series—a strange chain of tiny depressions between two bigger craters called Copernicus and Eratosthenes in the central region of the Moon—which seems much too regular to have been caused by the random impact of meteorites.

Nor does it seem likely that they were formed by boulders flung out from Copernicus' mouth when the big crater erupted.

They look much more like explosion craters, lined up along some fissure, through which volcanic gases could have burst.

The riddles pile up, one on another. Not until robot spacecraft have drilled out samples of rock, analysed them and radioed their findings back to Earth; not until satellites carrying television cameras have orbited close to the lunar surface, or astronauts actually set foot on the terrain, can anyone be *sure* they know the answers to them.

All we know now is that the Moon is a very unfriendly place for humans to go; and, we know with equal certainty, that they *will* go there.

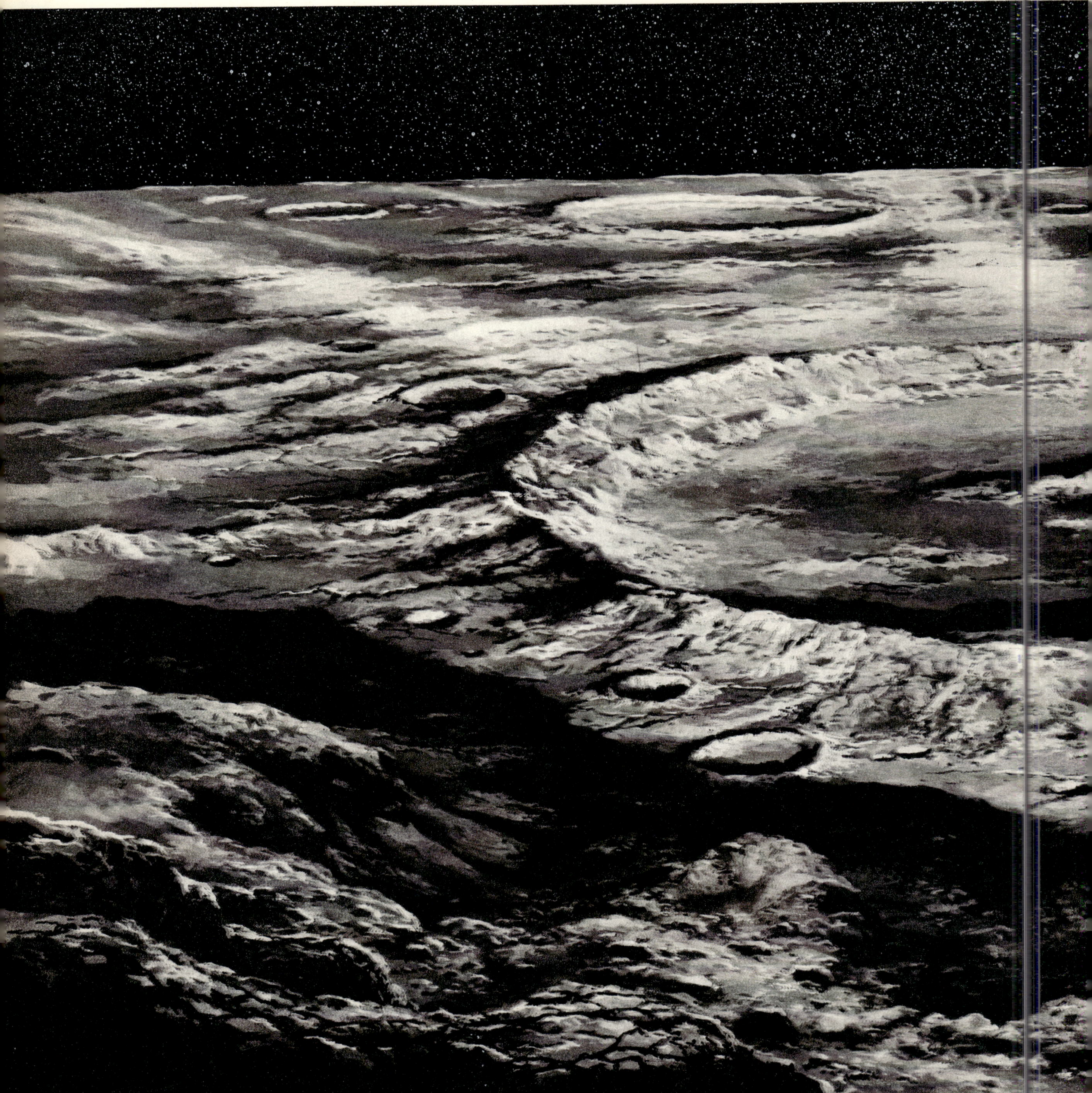

17. *A lunar crater, with light-coloured rays*

VENUS

Our next port of call is Venus. If we think that the Moon has puzzling features, they are nothing compared with those of Venus.

We know hardly anything about the planet's face, for no man has ever seen it, even through a telescope. It is shrouded perpetually by clouds.

We know Venus comes closer to Earth than any other Planet—to within 26 million miles—and that when it approaches us it shines as one of the brightest objects in the sky. Its reflectivity is about 60 per cent compared with the Moon's 7 per cent.

If it is west of the Sun Venus appears as a 'morning star', and if to the east, as an 'evening star'.

We know that it is slightly smaller than our own planet. Recently its mass was measured very precisely—0.81485 times that of the Earth.

For a long time it was thought that Venus rotated on its axis every 13 days or so: in other words that night and day there each lasted nearly one Earth week. But modern radar techniques of 'bouncing' signals between Earth and Venus and catching the 'echoes' in radio-telescopes have now enabled the rotational period to be fixed at about *250 days*.

In other words, Venus turns very, very slowly indeed. Since it takes only 225 days to orbit the Sun, the planet's 'nights' and 'days' actually go in the reverse way to ours.

From the slow speed of turn—and from the fact that it is an average of 25.6 million miles nearer to the Sun than we—we can deduce that it is a very hot place. But more about the temperature later.

What else do we know? That it is travelling through space at 78,300 miles per hour and that it is a planet without natural satellites.

It is at this point that the riddles begin to confront us, and argument starts.

Why are those clouds there? What are they made of? Just how hot is Venus? Could it support life in any form? Why does it rotate so slowly by comparison with Earth?

When astronomers first turned their telescopes and spectroscopes—instruments which identify materials from the way in which they absorb and give out light—on Venus they recorded a lot of carbon-dioxide gas in its atmosphere. There was also some nitrogen, but apparently no oxygen or water vapour there.

Then they realised that the planet's clouds were not white as they are on Earth—but yellowish. So they assumed that natural conditions must be quite different from those on our own planet, either in the present or past.

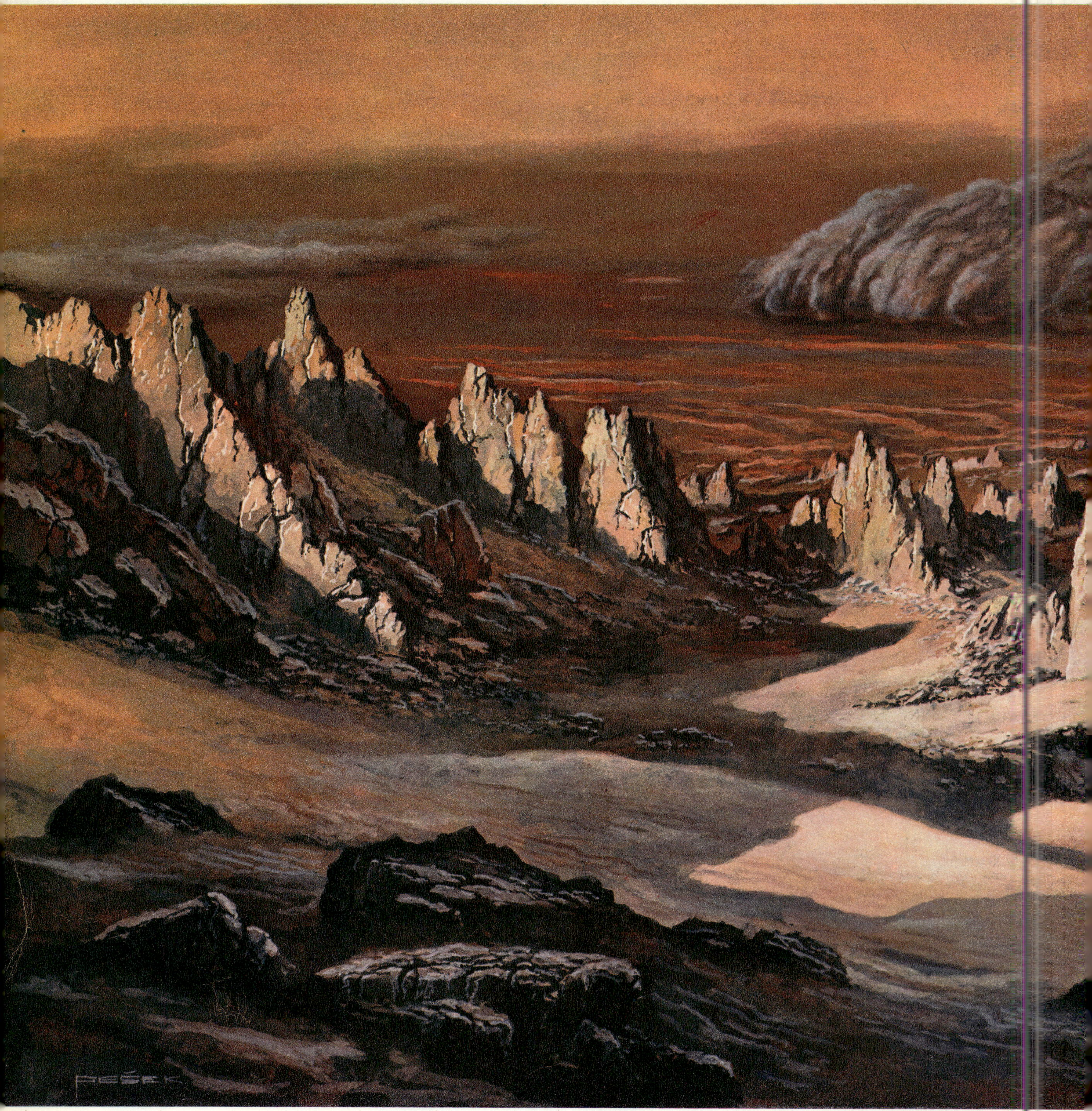
PEŠEK

18. *'Hundreds of miles of desolate, burned-out terrain, rocky plains and bare, brightly coloured rocks'*
   ...that is Venus

Some claimed that Venus must be a huge swamp composed of liquid carbohydrates and that the 'clouds' were really an oily smog. Others suggested the clouds were formed from minute droplets of formaldehyde—the chemical widely used in laboratories for preserving human or animal tissue and organs.

Another hypothesis was that they were clouds of dust. Those who held this view reasoned that since no water could be detected on Venus its whole surface must be a huge parched desert: or that, even if there had *once* been water, it had all evaporated, and the once fertile countryside had become arid.

Dust from dried out, disintegrating rocks and particles of salts had risen to form opaque clouds, they said.

Other scientists were not happy with any of these explanations.

They put forward an entirely contrary theory: that Venus *had* water—lots of it—in fact, that the entire surface was covered by oceans.

How, then, did they explain the failure of spectroscopes to detect any water vapour? In two ways. Firstly, they said, their 'readings' might have been confused and blurred by our own atmosphere as they looked out at Venus. Secondly, that the outermost layers of Venus' clouds were probably made up of microscopic ice crystals and that these were shielding the presence of water below.

As evidence, they pointed to the fact that the temperature of the upper clouds was certainly very low—between 35 and 40 degrees Fahrenheit below freezing. (It is interesting to note that this temperature matches that of the highest layers of cumulus cloud over the Earth, above which water cannot exist in liquid form.)

The idea of a covering of water fitted in nicely, too, with the picture of Venus obtained when it was viewed through certain colour filters. For when Venus was studied in red and yellow light, it had all the qualities of a mirror; and water reflects like a mirror.

Still more support was found for the oceanic model.

It explained, the claim went on, why so much carbon dioxide showed up in the planet's atmosphere. This gas is normally absorbed by rocks and turned into carbonates: yet on Venus this did not appear to happen. Something—some layer—must be stopping it from coming into contact with the mineral surfaces; and this layer could well be water.

The theory took a severe battering when, in the late 1950's, radio-telescopes began to detect temperatures of more than 600 degrees Fahrenheit at or near Venus's surface.

These at once appeared to rule out the possibility of any water existing today on the face of the planet; but they did not rule out

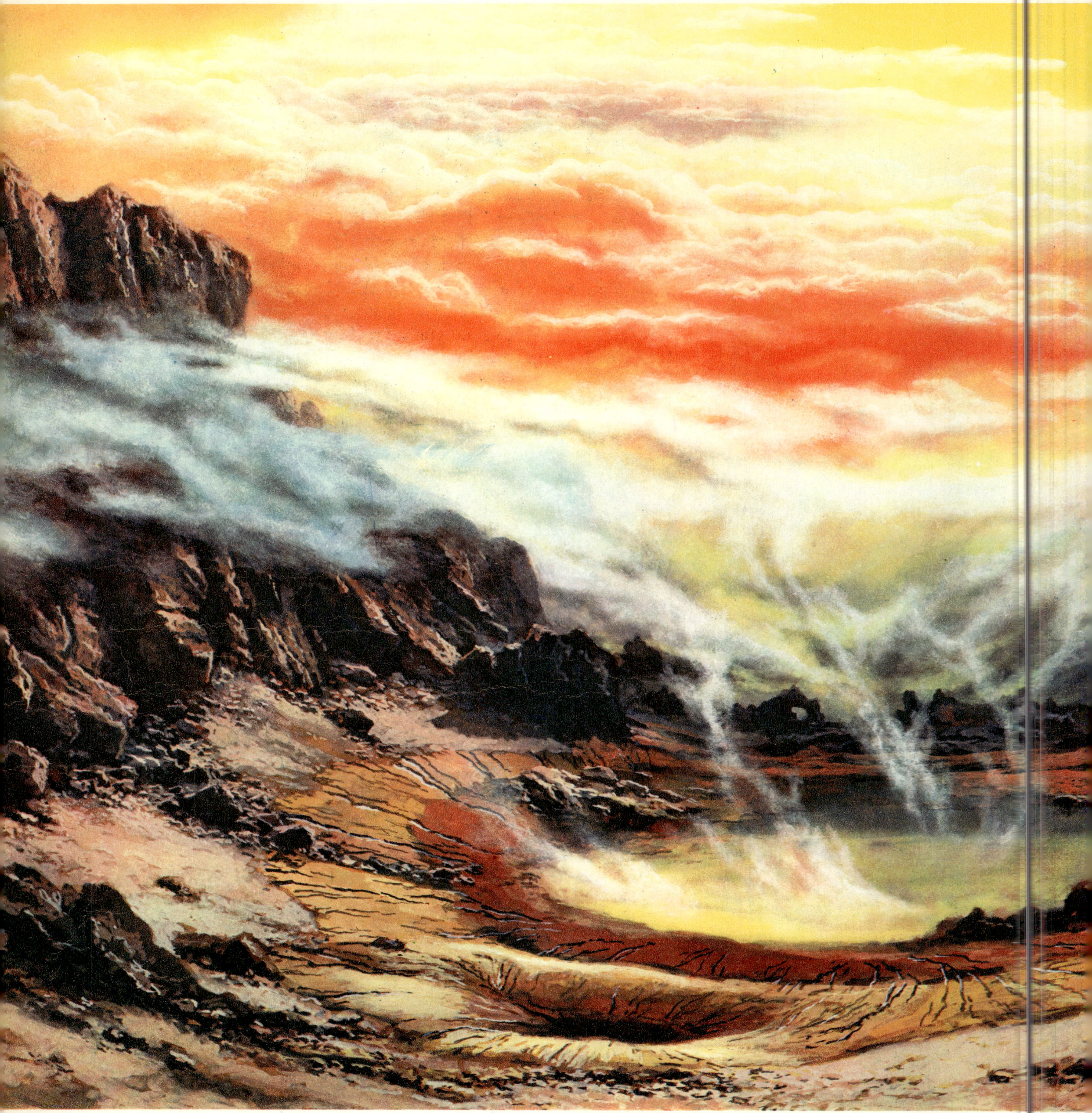

19. Venus, the planet no man has seen because of the thick clouds that shroud it

the possibility of water having once existed, and having evaporated since to form the dense clouds.

The big conundrum then became: why is Venus so hot?

Some said it was because high winds and dust were causing friction on the surface and that this was responsible for the heat.

Others suggested that the temperature reading might be false—upset by, say, a layer of electrically-charged particles around Venus, much thicker than that surrounding our own planet.

A large number of scientists supported a theory that Venus was a gigantic 'greenhouse'—that the clouds were of carbon-dioxide gas which would let in sunlight like panes of glass but prevent heat from being reflected back into space. But this theory depended on there being water vapour present in the atmosphere.

It was in the midst of all this argument that a tiny robot spacecraft blasted off from Cape Canaveral, Florida, U.S.A. on August 27th, 1962. Destination: the 'mystery planet' Venus itself.

The space craft was called Mariner Two.

Its predecessor, Mariner One, had had to be destroyed after five minutes of flight when it veered dangerously off course.

America was not the first nation to attempt to send a spacecraft to Venus. Soviet scientists had launched a much bigger craft, weighing 1,419 pounds, on the very same journey in February 1961.

It is believed to have passed within 62,500 miles of the planet in May that year, but unfortunately all radio contact with it was lost after a fortnight.

The new Mariner soared aloft beautifully, its Atlas booster rocket belching a fat tongue of flame.

It went once round the Earth, attached to a second rocket called Agena, and was then flung outwards into space at a speed of 25,700 m.p.h.

It escaped the clutch of gravity and settled down to a long voyage towards the planet which has often been called Earth's twin.

Mariner was aimed not to hit Venus but to pass by it at a distance of 10,000 miles. This was decided in order to allow a 'look' to be taken at conditions around the back of Venus as well as on its face.

Mariner was able to scan the planet for 35 minutes. If it had been directed right on to it—as Russia's Lunik was directed on to the Moon—this observation time would have been considerably shortened.

The American robot, looking rather like a giant moth with 'wings' of solar cells to catch the sun's energy and turn it into electrical power, reached Venus on December 14th, 1962.

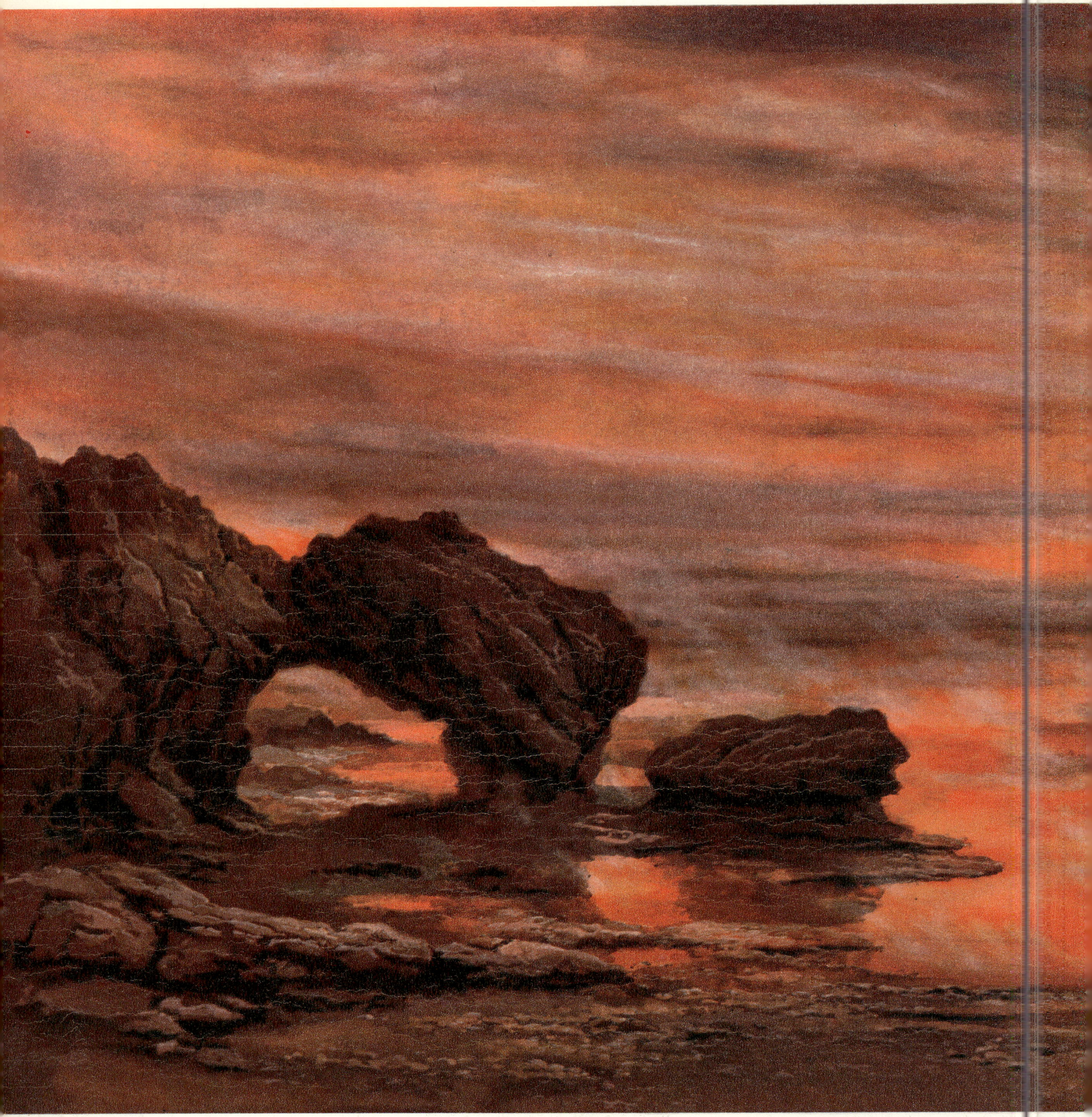

20. *A dried-out sea on Venus*

It had covered 180,200,000 miles in its 3½-month journey, although Venus at the time was only about 36,000,000 miles from Earth. A long, arching trajectory had to be followed to conserve fuel and to bring planet and spacecraft together at the right moment.

En route, Mariner recorded low levels of radiation in space, even during periods when a flare burst out on the face of the Sun, and from this scientists were able to deduce that men could have made the same journey without harm.

The spacecraft actually missed Venus by a greater distance than intended—by an extra 11,594 miles—but it was still close enough to carry out all its planned tasks.

What shooting! An error of less than 12,000 miles in a journey of 180,000,000.

On the afternoon of December 14th, scientists at the American tracking station at Goldstone, California, pulsed a tiny, energised signal out through space from an 85-foot diameter, dish-shaped aerial. The energy triggered a switch inside Mariner, and instruments aboard began to do their detective work...

Mariner carried six scientific experiments attached to its frame. One involved the use of a device called a microwave radiometer and was intended to record the temperature on the surface of Venus, and details of its atmosphere. The second—using an infra-red radiometer—was to determine any fine structure in the layers of cloud around the planet.

The third—involving a magnetometer—was to measure the presence and strength of any magnetic field around Venus. Such a field might be expected to hold charged particles in its clutch and give Venus radiation belts like the Earth's.

The fourth was to measure the intensity of these particles—if they were there. To do this, scientists fitted Mariner with two little pieces of apparatus called an ion chamber and a particle flux detector.

The fifth and sixth experiments were switched on throughout the flight and were intended to reveal facts about conditions in interplanetary space rather than near Venus itself.

One measured how much dust Mariner encountered, and the direction in which it was moving. It found, incidentally, that the dust was 1,000 times thicker near Earth than in deep space, thus tending to confirm the theory that planets concentrate this cosmic debris near themselves.

The other experiment recorded radiation coming from the Sun.

It was 7:59 p.m. on December 14th in London when the little spacecraft began making history...

Up until that moment, the most reliable evidence about

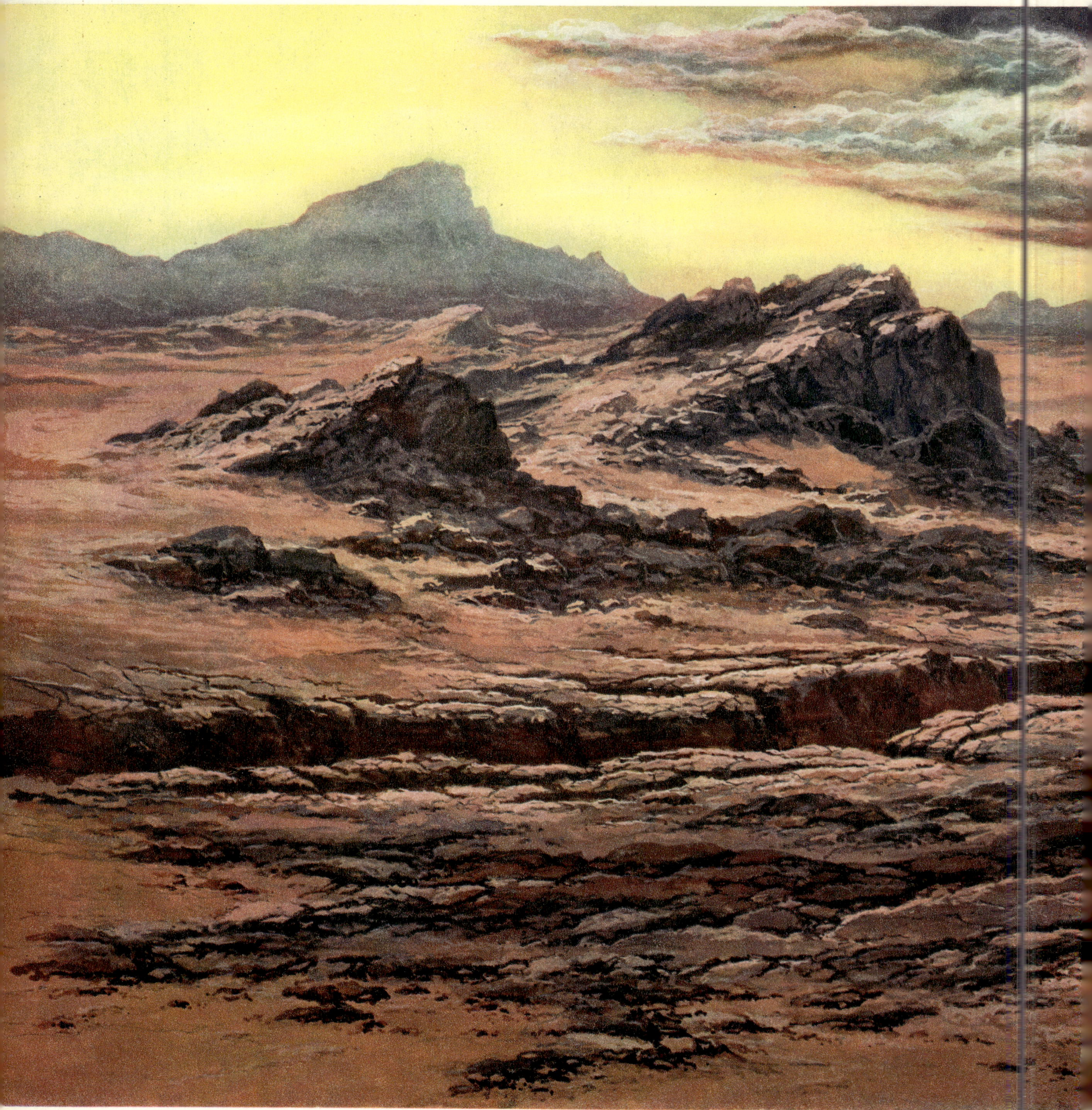

21. *Landscape in the tropical region of Venus*

conditions on Venus had come from a group of American astronomers who, in 1959, despatched a spectroscope 38 miles up into the sky in the basket of a balloon.

This spectroscope—with only a thin layer of atmosphere between it and Venus to distort its pictures—had found plenty of water vapour in the Venusian clouds.

Accordingly, I had adjusted my mental picture of conditions on the planet to look like this:

Constant darkness or, at best, a sort of twilight. An atmosphere heavy with water vapour, shrouding the Sun into a faint spot, and making breathing difficult. Never-ending heat. A little rain, perhaps, in the polar regions at night; but evaporating as soon as morning comes. Hundreds of miles of desolate, burned-out terrain, rocky plains, and bare brightly coloured rocks—making our own Sahara Desert seem a paradise by comparison.

I visualised the predominant colour as red, because of the presence of iron oxide in the rocks, but it would barely be discernible in the gloom.

I considered that it was just possible for some form of life to exist in parts where rain might gather; but that this life, if it existed, would be primitive—plants, algae or perhaps some single-celled organisms.

How accurate was this vision?

It took several months of work with computers to decipher and analyse the stream of data sent back by Mariner during its 35-minute 'fly-by', and when the answers came they were something of a shock.

The first important finding was that the surface temperature of Venus was even hotter than previous measurements had suggested—about 800 degrees Fahrenheit, compared with 615 degrees Fahrenheit suggested by radio-telescopes on Earth.

This clearly was far too hot to allow any water to lie on the planet itself, and far too hot to permit life in any form—at least, in any form imaginable by Man.

Mariner's second discovery was that the temperature of the cloud layer on the 'dark' side of Venus was the same as on the sunlit side. Above the very centre of the planet it was minus 30 degrees Fahrenheit. But there was one curious anomaly: in the southern half of Venus there was a particularly cold spot— about 20 degrees Fahrenheit colder than the rest of the cloud layer.

This meant that the clouds at this spot were higher or more opaque, or both. It suggested that below them might lie an unusual surface feature, such as a big mountain.

A third surprise came when the results of the magnetometer

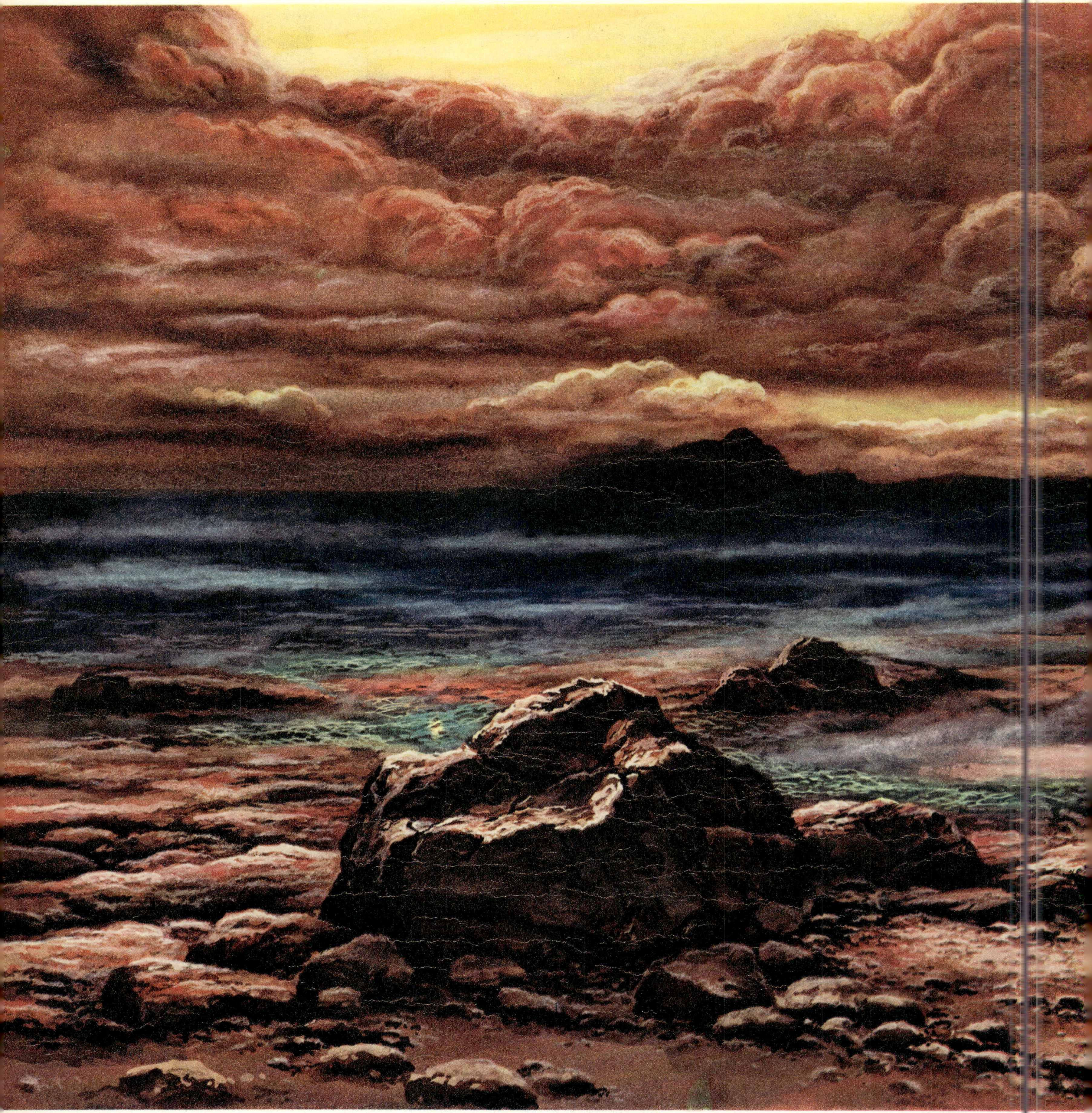

22. *This was how I visualised Venus before America's Mariner spacecraft found temperatures too high to support water on the planet*

experiment aboard Mariner were analysed. No trace of a magnetic field around the planet could be found.

American scientists admitted that their instrument was not sensitive enough to rule out the possibility of a weak field existing near the surface, but it was certainly not comparable with our own.

Why—if Venus is so similar in size to our planet as to earn the nickname 'Earth's Twin'—does it not have a similar magnetic field?

A key factor seems to be the rate at which planets spin. Venus, as we now know, rotates slowly. So does the Moon; and measurements made by one of Russia's Lunik space probes show that the lunar magnetic field is less than a third of one per cent of our own.

Jupiter, by contrast, spins rapidly—twice as fast as the Earth. Recent experiments suggest that *its* magnetic field is considerably stronger than ours.

Observations made so far, then, suggest that all planets and satellites which rotate less rapidly than the Earth have small magnetic fields; and this is consistent with theories which link these fields with a dynamo action inside the molten cores of the spinning planets.

Slow-turning planets are therefore unlikely to be surrounded by belts of trapped radiation as the Earth is.

This absence of radiation was confirmed in the case of Venus by the ion chamber and particle flux detector aboard Mariner.

These instruments recorded an average of only one charged particle per second when the spacecraft was closest to Venus. This compares with a rate of several thousand particles per second at the same distance from Earth.

Mariner's final surprise was to detect no carbon dioxide gas at all in the region of Venus' atmosphere that lies *above* its clouds, and no appreciable quantity of water vapour anywhere either.

From all this wealth of information it is now possible to say for certain that Venus is a very inhospitable planet indeed.

It is extremely hot. It is certainly barren of plants, insects or organisms as we recognise them. It is probably a gigantic dust bowl.

There are still many mysteries to explain—that unusually cold spot in the atmosphere for one—and scientists will not be happy about the reliability of Mariner's information until it is confirmed by subsequent space probes or perhaps, even, by men. But at least some of the clouds—to use a metaphor—have rolled away.

Mariner has now gone on to become a tiny, man-made planet of the Sun, its job magnificently done.

MERCURY

We now move to Mercury.

Venus proved to be an unfriendly place, but we do not require another Mariner to tell us that Mercury is even less attractive from the visitor's viewpoint.

For one thing it is the planet which is closest to the Sun—orbiting it at an average distance of 36,000,000 miles. The heat, therefore, must be scorching and probably of the order of 790 degrees Fahrenheit (420 degrees Centigrade) on the surface.

This is higher than the melting point of lead, and it is clear that if men are ever to get to Mercury their spaceships will have to be made of extremely tough materials, and refrigerated inside.

Another important feature of Mercury is that it spins on its axis once every 88 days, which is exactly the time it takes to revolve around the Sun. It thus keeps the same face pointed to the Sun all the time.

One side of Mercury, in consequence, is extremely hot; the other, very cold.

The planet does, however, 'wobble' a little—fluctuating in its orbit rather like the Moon. Just as there are certain regions of the Moon which are only visible to us during these *librations*, as they are called, so there is a border-line area of Mercury which is alternately in sunshine and darkness.

This area is called the *terminator* or *twilight zone*.

There, it would be possible to escape from the murderous glare and heat for a while without freezing to death. There, the shadows would lengthen and diminish. There, one could take a good look around.

23. Mercury — 'There are large craters, parched deserts and probably a multitude of cliffs...' >

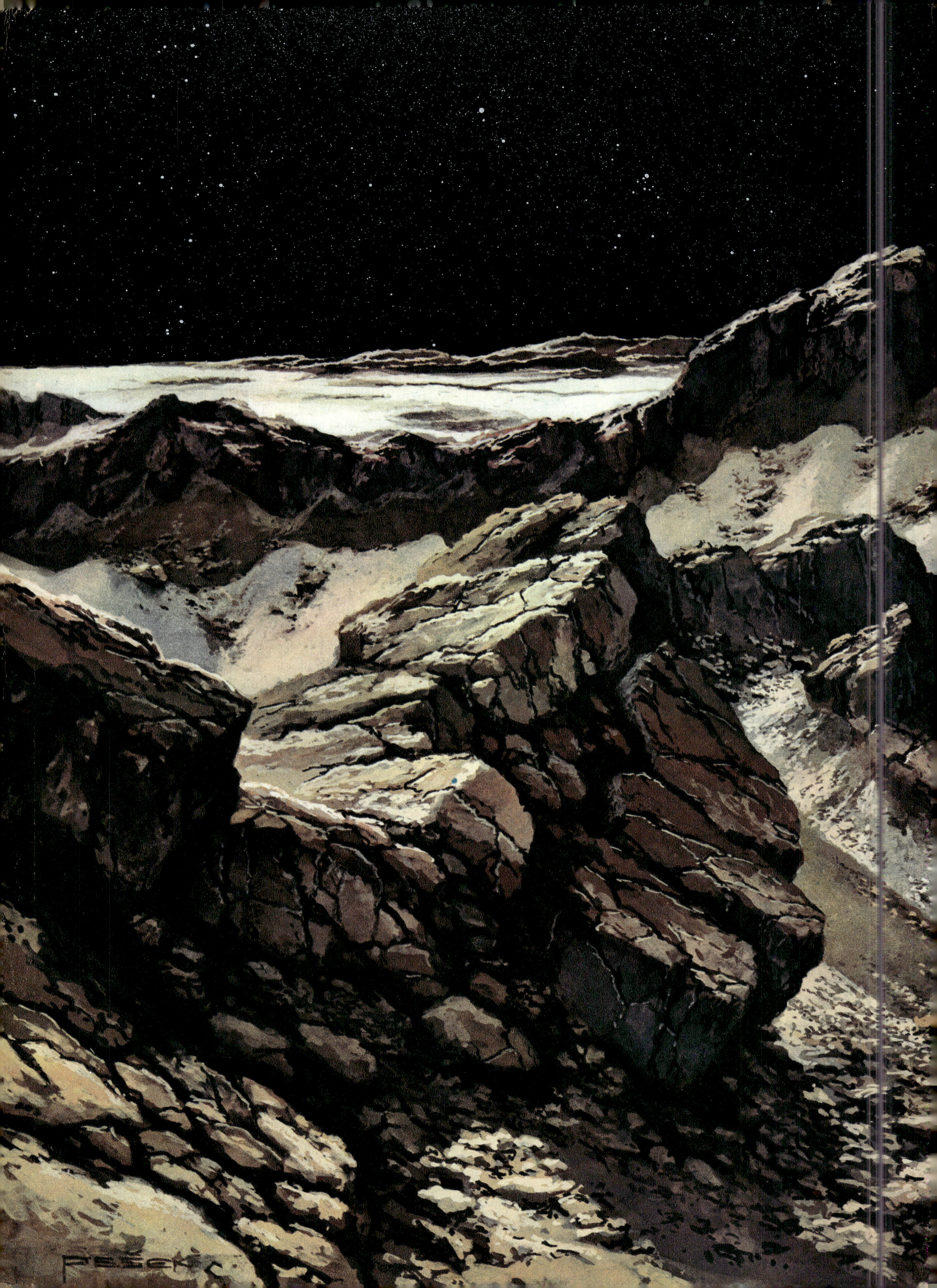

From Mercury the Sun would appear three times larger than it does to us on Earth, and Venus would shine brightly enough to cast shadows of its own.

The Earth would be visible—but it would look no bigger than Jupiter does from our planet. One could watch the Moon orbiting the Earth, without the aid of a telescope.

All the other planets—Jupiter, Saturn, Uranus, Neptune, Pluto and Mars—would seem rather dim, because of their distance.

If astronauts could only get there, the back of Mercury would be an ideal astronomical observation post—even better than the Moon. From here it should be possible to take some wonderful pictures of comets—clearer and brighter than any so far recorded on Earth. But, away from the sunlight, astronomers would have to cope with intense cold: the temperature on Mercury's dark side is probably as low as minus 410 degrees Fahrenheit (minus 245 degrees Centigrade).

The planet measures 3,200 miles across, and its surface bears some resemblance to the Moon. There are large craters, parched deserts and probably a multitude of cliffs. But all the rock formations are sure to be in a much more advanced stage of deterioration than on the Moon because the Sun sends more energy into the surface.

The danger to astronauts from radiation is correspondingly greater.

The 19th-century German astronomer Johann Schroter claimed to have detected a mountain on Mercury at one point during his observations, and he thought this might well be 11 miles high.

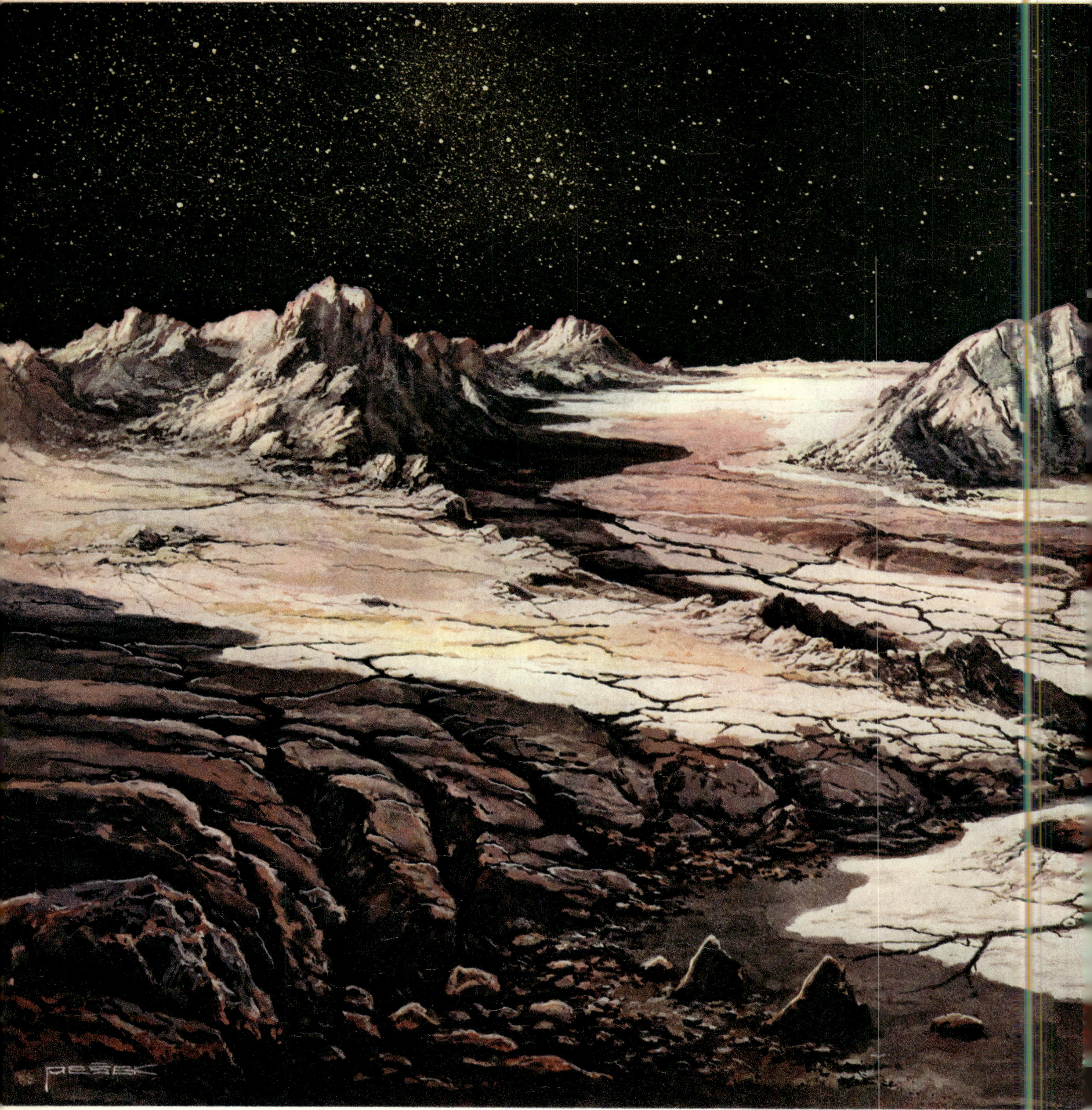

24. *Close-up of Mercury's cliffs with desert in the background*

But subsequent studies suggest that this was an over-estimate.

To anyone walking on the planet the sky would appear to be a shade less black than on, say, the Moon. This is because there seems to be a very faint haze covering Mercury. Exactly what this is, no one is sure—but recent research suggests that it may be a very weak atmosphere, with a density of only one three-hundredth of that of the Earth.

The pressure created by this tenuous layer of gas is probably about equal to the pressure in our own atmosphere 29 miles above ground. The haze could explain why we have only been able to make poor maps of Mercury up till now. Sometimes the surface details appear to disappear completely behind dark spots.

The opacity of the gas haze would be enhanced by radiation from the Sun. It can be shown that the Sun will cause very thin atmospheres to luminesce, and the 'glow' in the mist would certainly tend to make details less sharp to the observer.

I have said that Mercury's dark side would make an excellent astronomical observation post because other objects in the heavens would stand out so vividly. An additional reason is that—because of the planet's slow spin—it would take the equivalent of 44 Earth days for a star to travel across its sky, thus giving the observer plenty of time to study it.

But such attractions are heavily outweighed by the hostility of Mercury's environment and I venture to say that no man will ever consider it worth the risk to go there.

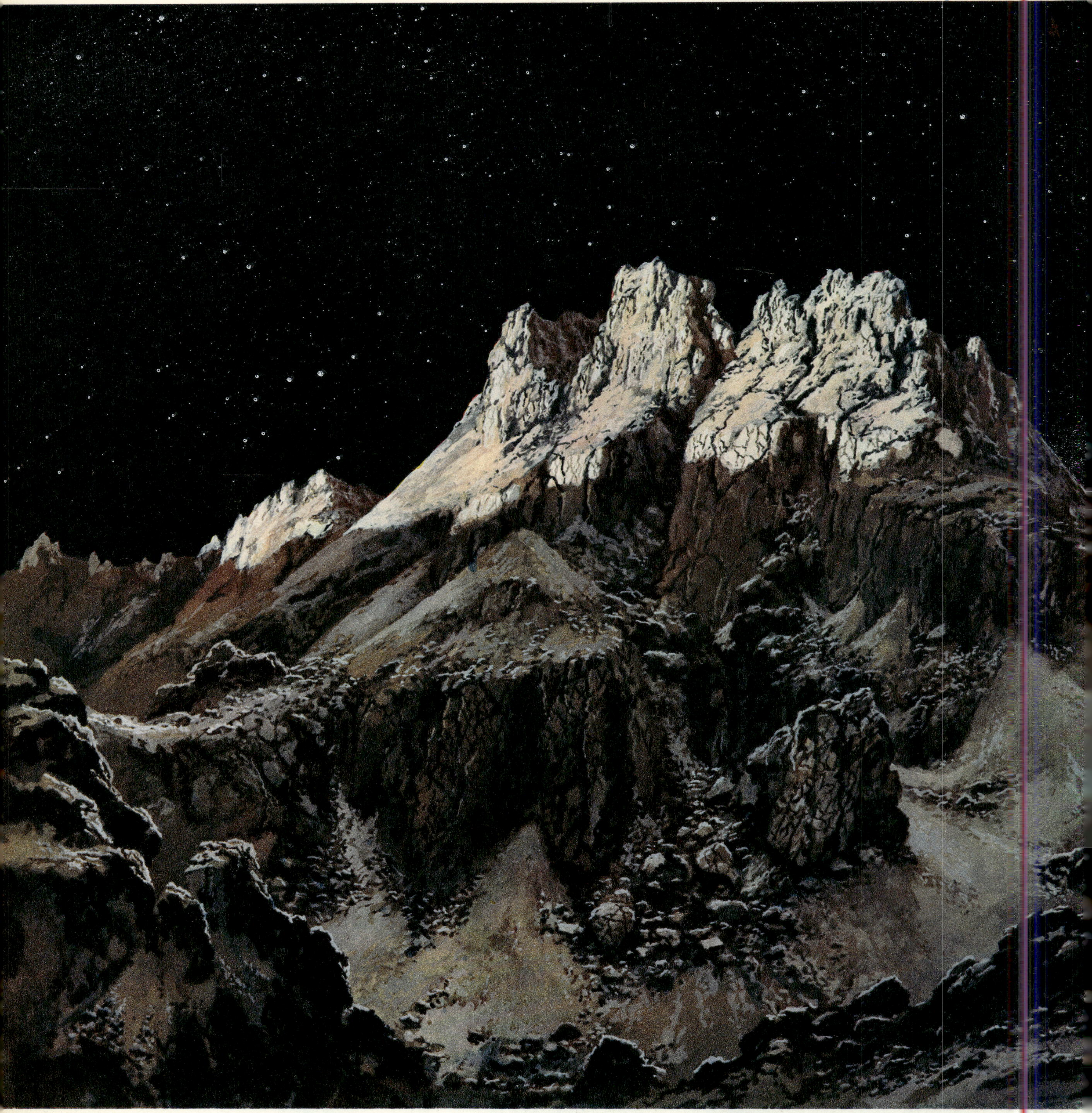

25. *Mercury, as it might look in the 'Twilight Zone'*

MARS

There is no question in my mind that men will go to Mars. Plans for them to do so in the 1980s are already laid.

The round trip from Earth will be long and arduous—covering more than 300 million miles of space and lasting at least 19 months, but the rewards will be great.

The flight will call for the development of more advanced forms of propulsion than the chemical rocket—probably nuclear or electric power. But such technology is already developing, and it is safe to assume that when Man has learned enough about *his* side of the operation to risk travelling over such huge distances he will not be frustrated by want of an engine.

In the meantime, efforts are being made to precede him with robot spacecraft laden with cameras and ingenious instruments.

Mars interests scientists a great deal because it appears to be the planet most likely to contain a form of life recognisable to human intelligence. It also resembles the Earth in that it has an atmosphere; but it is considerably smaller than our own planet.

It comes fairly close to us—to within 35 million miles—and when it does it appears as a very bright object indeed. Much of Mars is reddish in colour, and this has given rise to its nickname, the Red Planet. The colour also led to its being called after the mythological god of war.

In 1877 an American astronomer named Asaph Hall noticed two pinpoints of light moving around Mars. These were subsequently proved to be satellites, and they were given the names Phobos and Deimos. They are small—Phobos about 12 miles in diameter and Deimos approximately 5—and are probably asteroids which have been captured in Mars's gravitational field.

The presence of such captive rocks is not surprising, since the region of space between Mars's and Jupiter's orbits contains many thousands of asteroids, thought to be the remnants of collisions between full-sized planets.

If astronauts were to land on, say, Deimos—which orbits Mars at a distance of 12,500 miles—they could expect to find a broken and cracked surface, with uneven edges and sharp breaks, much more reminiscent of a rock fragment than a true moon.

The gravity there would be imperceptible, the horizon only a few hundred yards away—no matter where the eye travelled.

It is quite possible that Deimos still bears scars from its birth millions of years ago—craters formed by impact with another object whirling around the Sun. If it was originally part of a big planet, it might even contain some evidence of primitive life.

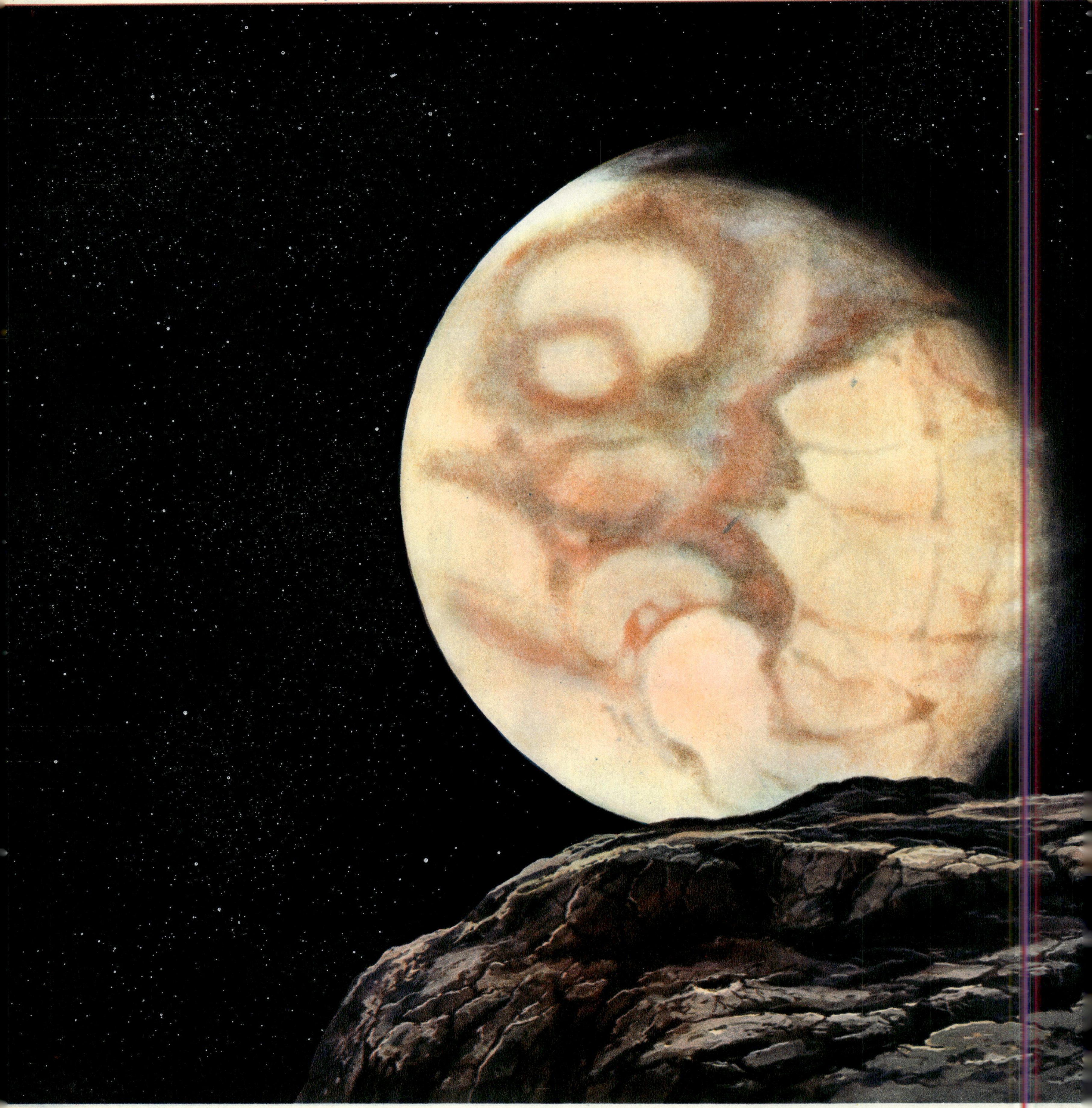

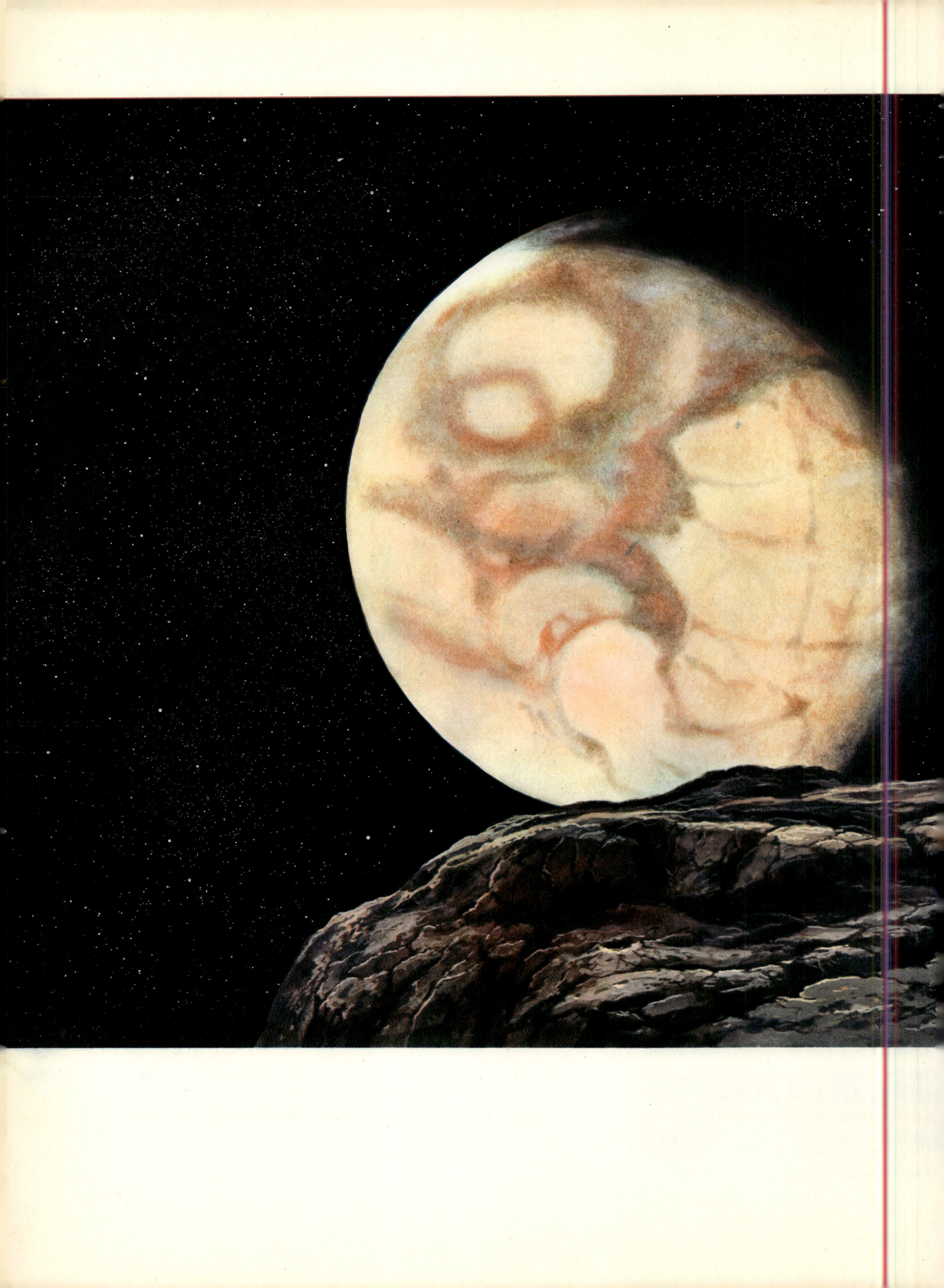

26. *Mars, as it might appear from one of its two satellites — Deimos*

Tell-tale traces of a low order of life have recently been found in certain stony meteorites which have tumbled to Earth from space, and Deimos could harbour more. Microscopes have revealed tiny little patterns in these meteorites which strongly resemble the fossilised remains of organisms such as *flagellae*; although the evidence is hotly disputed, it gives support to the idea that life *does* exist elsewhere than on Earth.

Whether it exists in Deimos's crust or not, it is quite likely to be present on Mars.

The Martian climate is cold and dry, but there is almost certainly some water on the surface; and water, as we know, is regarded by biologists as an essential condition for life.

The most reliable evidence about Mars's atmosphere was obtained in March 1963 when American scientists sent a telescope and spectroscope 79,000 feet above the Earth, fixed to a balloon. The instruments scanned the planet's surface five times and confirmed that the air there is thin—equivalent to that about 11 miles up over the Earth—and that it contains water vapour and some carbon dioxide. Also present were quantities of nitrogen and other gases such as methane and argon.

Little or no oxygen has ever been detected, and the atmospheric pressure at the surface is less than a ninth of our own.

The amount of water on Mars is probably small and mostly in a frozen state. Astronomers have noted white areas at both the planet's poles and these vary in size according to the season of the year.

In winter they expand, in spring they shrink rapidly, and in summer they are little more than white spots. The conclusion is that they are frozen areas similar to our own polar caps. But the speed at which they shrink—about 160 miles a day—suggests that they are more like thin layers of hoar frost.

As the warm Sun strikes them they probably turn directly into water vapour rather than liquid pools. The vapour is then hungrily absorbed by the atmosphere. This seasonal replenishment of the cold dry Martian air with water vapour seems to be one of the meteorological processes on the planet. It sets currents or winds moving, and these carry the moisture down into the equatorial regions.

Ice crystals may even fall to the surface, awakening life...

Some scientists maintain that the climate was once more temperate and that seas and oceans used to lie across the surface.

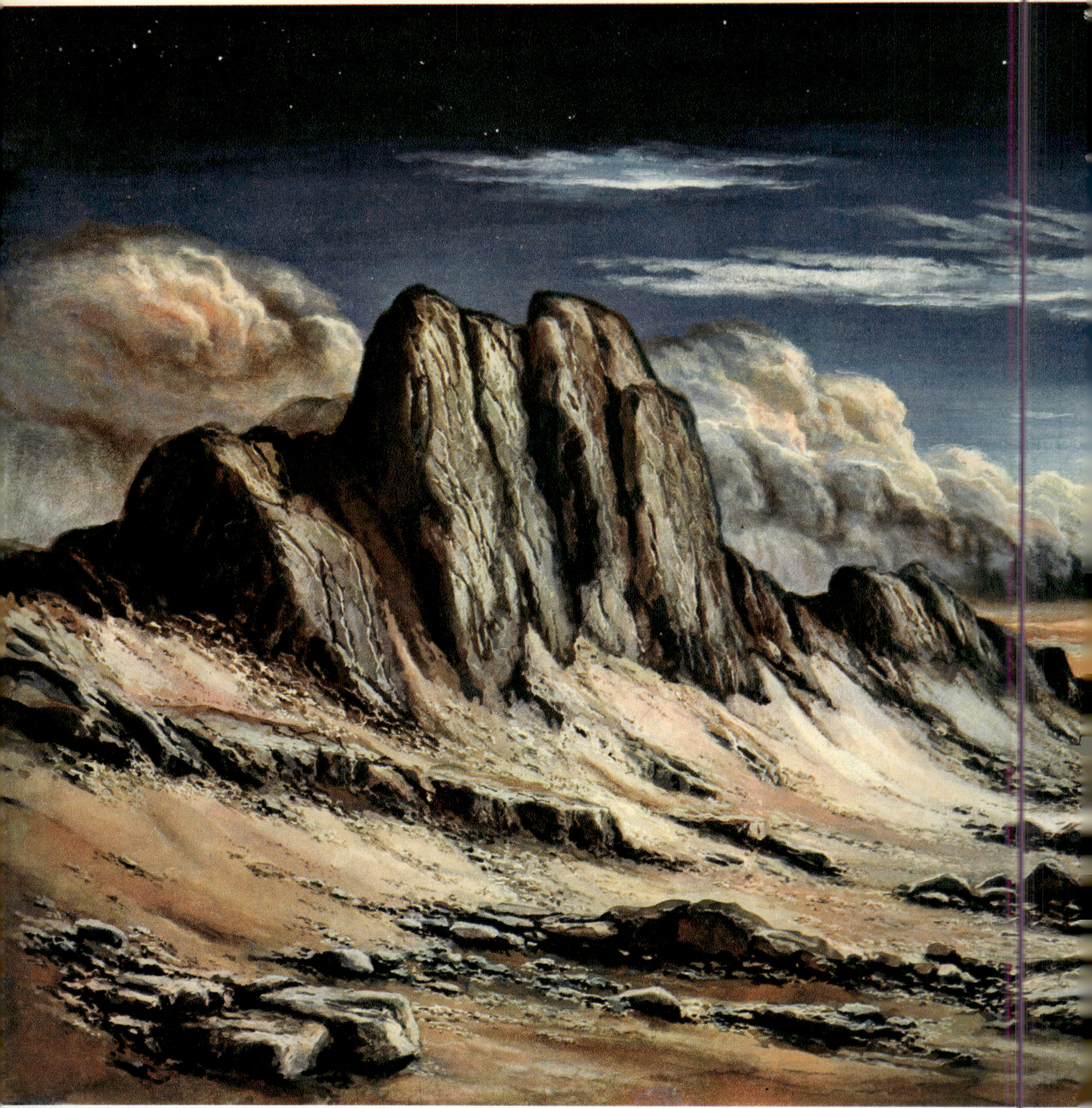

27. '*Old Martian mountains, now severely eroded, whose crumbling cliffs are slowly being blown down into the plains…*'

This is hard to prove or disprove. Much of Mars is today buried in what looks like dust, and any seas which may once have existed would by now have become subterranean icebergs.

We must await the arrival of astronauts to find out the truth.

The climate there today is certainly not very pleasant. In the summer, daytime temperatures rise only a few degrees above freezing, and at night they drop to minus 60 degrees Fahrenheit or lower. It might well be asked why they do not fall even lower, as they do on our Moon: the answer is that a thin ice mist forms over the planet on cold nights, trapping some of the surface heat and preventing it from radiating out into the black pit of space.

These thin mists show up sometimes to Earth-based astronomers as white areas near the edge of the planet when it is just being illuminated by the morning Sun. As the Sun rises the fogs disappear without a trace.

The whole of Mars is divided up into light and dark areas, and patches of varying hue. Some are reddish, some grey-green, some brown, and the fascinating thing about them is that they change colour and size according to the season.

It is this phenomenon which prompts many scientists to believe that they are evidence of *life*.

The red areas—covering about three-fifths of the planet's surface—are believed to be flat deserts covered with a fine dust. Modern instruments indicate that the dust is actually powdered iron oxide. Dark spots on these deserts may well be remnants of prominences in the terrain—old mountains, now severely eroded, whose crumbling cliffs are being slowly blown down into the plains. Thus the whole planet is slowly turning into one gigantic desert.

Dust storms are frequent—particularly early in summer—and can be seen from the Earth. One such storm, observed in 1911, appeared to cover almost the whole of the southern half of Mars.

Another big one blew up as recently as 1956. The clouds on these occasions take on a yellowish colour as well as their familiar ruddy hue.

How does the iron oxide come to be there? It is an intriguing problem.

Probably the Martian atmosphere once contained quite large amounts of oxygen, and this reacted with iron in the planet's crust to form brightly coloured oxides. But if this is so, how did the oxygen get there in the first place? And does this indicate that life was once at a much higher level there than it is today?

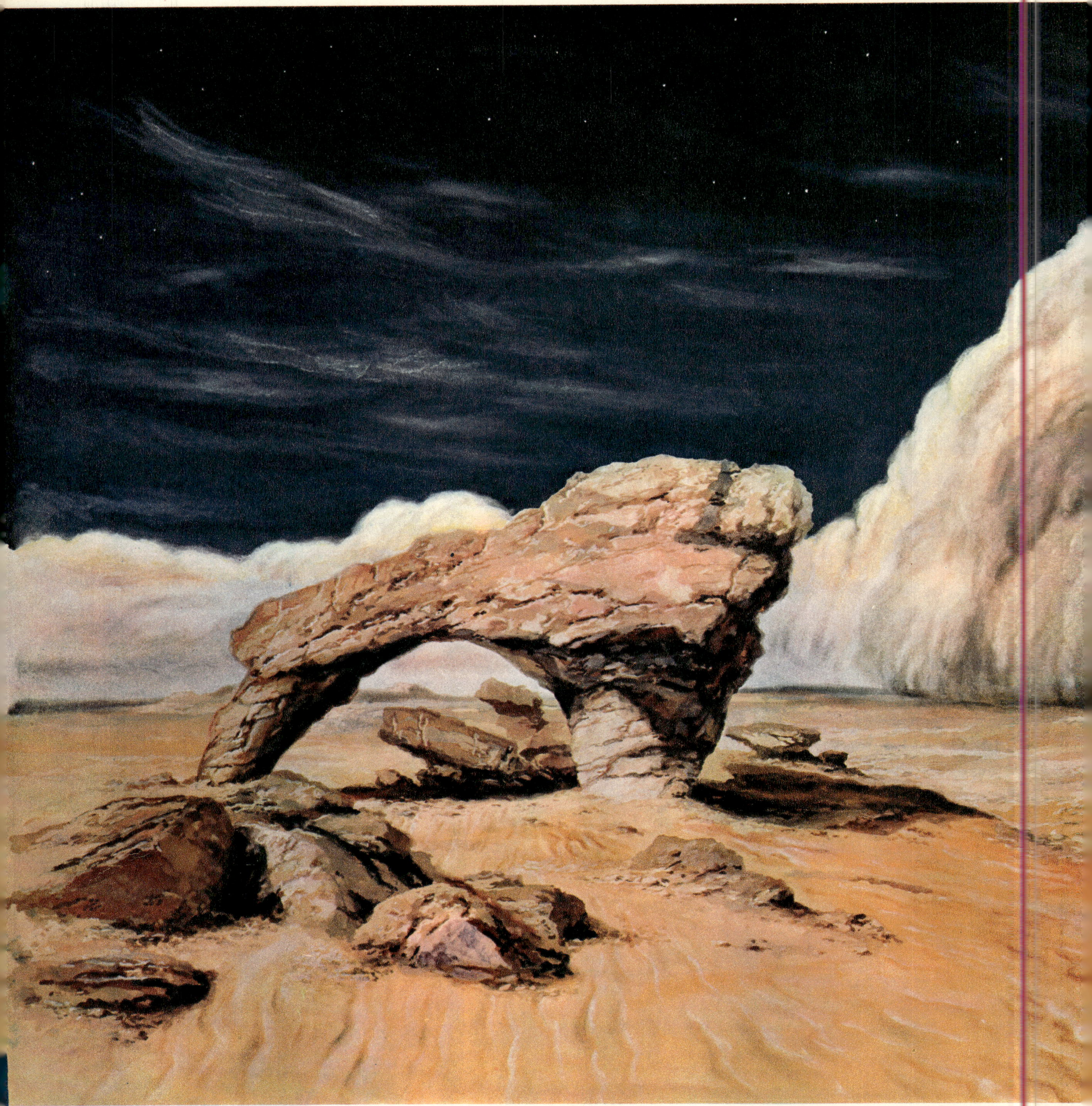

28. *'Much of Mars is today buried in what looks like dust'*

Nobody can answer these questions yet.

All that we know about life on Mars is that areas of the planet darken noticeably in spring and fade away almost to nothing in winter—suggesting that *something* is growing. Many experts suppose it to be a primitive form of vegetation, such as lichens—flowerless plants with a scaly texture and fronds—or microscopic algae.

But new evidence came to light recently when Mars was studied through special filters which masked all but the infra-red heat coming from the planet. These showed up traces of certain organic compounds which are the basic building-blocks for primitive life on Earth—life which can survive without oxygen.

Such *anaerobes*, as they are called—bacteria, yeasts and certain fungi—are believed by biologists to have been the very first organisms to appear on Earth. They were followed later by oxygen-breathing forms, but only after green plants had begun to release oxygen into the atmosphere during the process known as *photosynthesis*.

The absence of oxygen on Mars would not worry anaerobes. The planet may thus contain priceless evidence of how primeval life developed, and a trip there might afford the equivalent of a look into our own world's past.

Elaborate life-detection experiments are now being devised to go inside unmanned spacecraft which will be sent to land on Mars before 1970.

They include a package of instruments which can be dropped gently through the thin atmosphere on the end of a parachute and which, on impact, will automatically throw out long sticky strings.

Tiny winches inside the package will then wind in the strings to which—it is hoped—living organisms will have stuck.

Any organisms pulled in will drop into a canister containing a special broth, mixed with a radioactive form of carbon. They will eat the broth and grow—giving off carbon dioxide gas as they do so. But the gas will be tainted by radioactivity; so a small Geiger counter, placed in the canister should detect it.

Any clicking of the counter will be converted into a signal and radioed back to Earth, telling scientists that life is definitely there.

A most ingenious plan!

At the time of writing a Soviet spacecraft weighing $17^1/_2$ hundredweight was heading for the planet, carrying a television

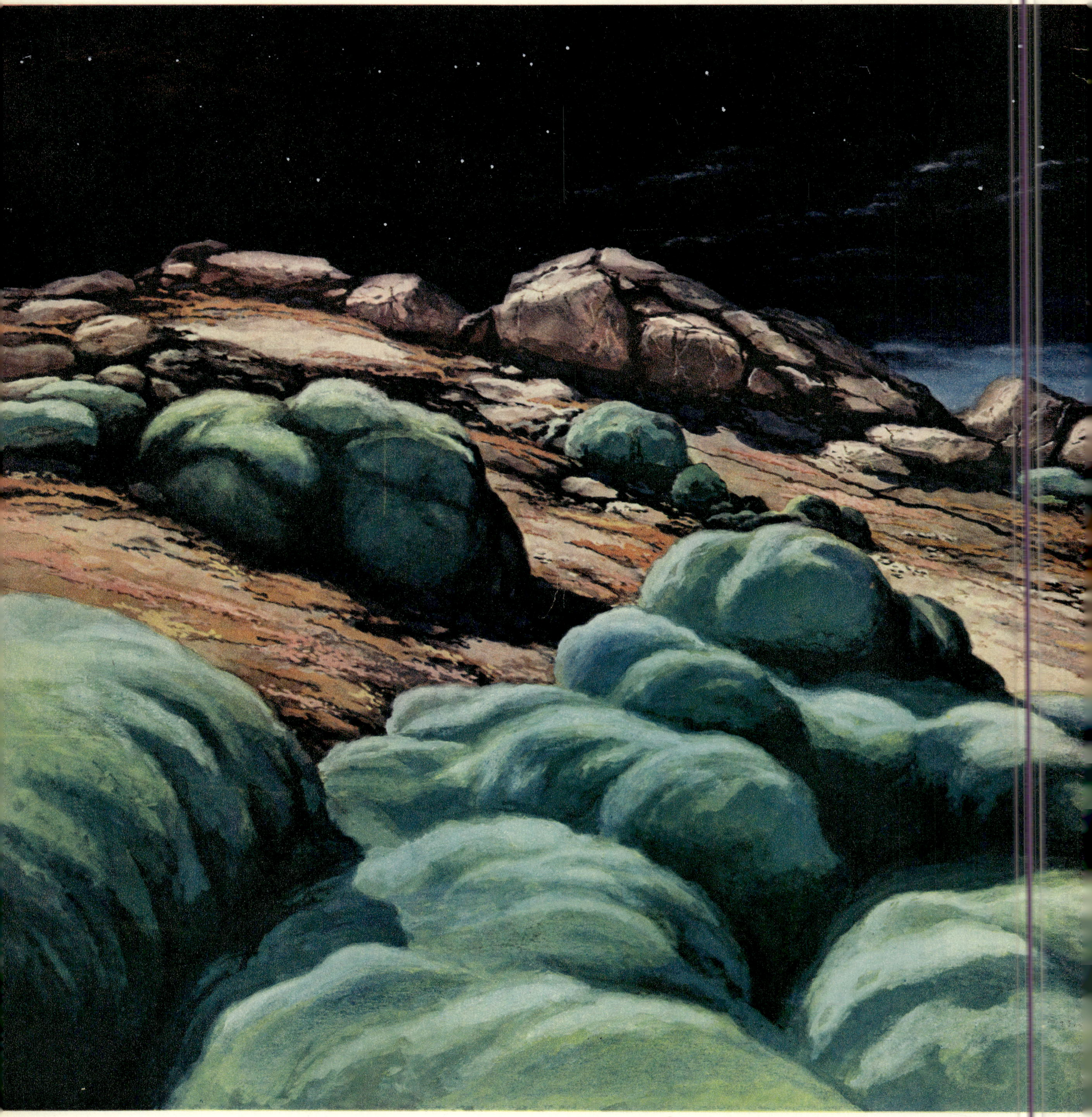

29. *'The whole planet (Mars) is slowly turning into a gigantic desert'*

camera, a radio-telescope, a spectroscope and magnetometers to measure any magnetic field around Mars.

After the craft had covered some 5 million miles in its 7-month-journey, scientists reported that it was likely to miss the Red Planet by a narrow margin.

It should pass close enough, however, to answer one of Mars's most tantalising riddles—what are those remarkably straight, dark grey lines which criss-cross its surface?

At the latter end of the 19th century the theory was put forward that they were a network of waterways—canals created by intelligent beings to irrigate the planet or transport boats. Where they crossed, exceptionally dark blobs could be seen: these were dubbed 'oases', and said to be centres of Martian population.

In 1901 an American astronomer named Lowell compiled a map of Mars which charted more than 400 canals, some 3,000 miles long.

Then observers began noticing that the canals seemed to be double, while on other occasions they became indecipherable.

To this day nobody has been able to explain them, except to say that it is highly unlikely that they are artificial—since Mars cannot be credited with intelligent life—and highly unlikely that they contain water.

Modern astronomers put them down to an optical illusion. They point out that over a distance of 26 million miles or more the human eye would tend to join up small surface features into hard lines. It is probable therefore that they are rocky outcrops, or uneven areas which happen to stand out rather vividly against the red desert sand.

Mars I, the Russian robot, should tell us.

In the meantime we have to content ourselves with a picture of the 4,260-mile-wide planet as a cold, windy, dusty place, smooth in parts, rough in others, with a fairly dark sky, wintry fogs, red earth, and a fascinating supply of tiny, moving organisms.

And these may hold the key to *our* very existence...

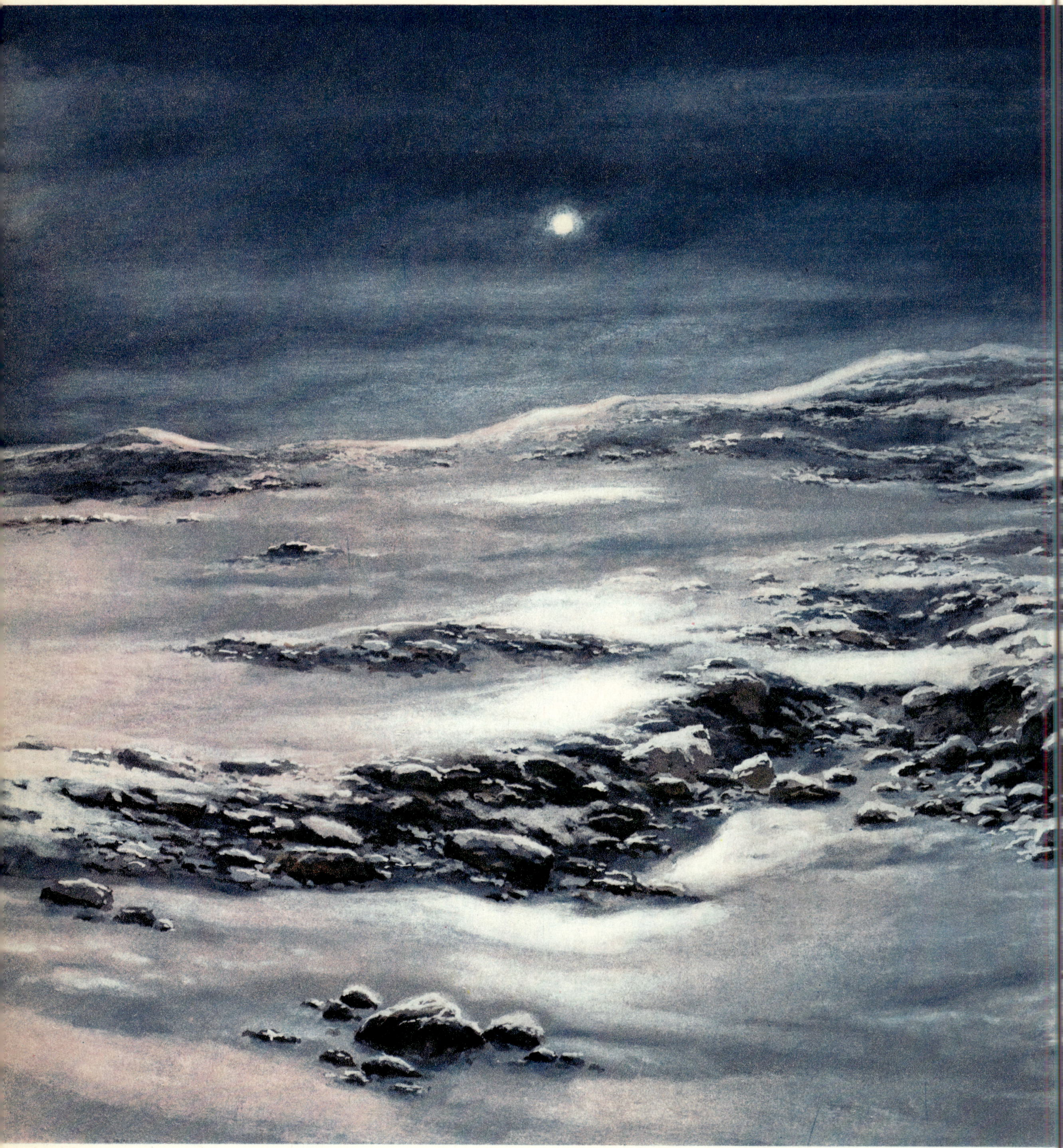

30. Mars — *'The water vapour is hungrily absorbed by the atmosphere'*

JUPITER

Mars—circling an average of 50 million miles farther away from the Sun than ourselves—was the last of the inner, or inferior, planets. It is probably also the last that Man will be able to reach unless a whole host of rocket propulsion and medical problems are solved.

Journeys to the outer, or superior planets, will take years, or even decades.

If they do become possible it is likely that explorers will make straight for Jupiter, the biggest of the planets and one of the brightest objects in our sky. If you visualise Jupiter as a hollow ball, it would be possible to put all the other planets in the Solar System inside it and still have a little room to spare.

But Jupiter ought not to be thought of as a hollow ball. We do not know how much of it is solid, or even that it has a solid centre at all.

All that we can see through our telescopes on Earth is the upper layer of Jupiter's atmosphere and 12 moons circling around it. Four of these moons are easily discernible with diameters ranging from about 3,220 to 1,960 miles. These four are closest to the planet, move from west to east, and take from 384 to 42 hours to go round it.

Three more moons are located at an average distance of 7,000,000 miles away. These, too, go from west to east. The others move in the opposite direction, and take an average of 700 days to orbit. They may well be asteroids.

Because we know nothing of what lies below Jupiter's dense atmosphere it would be advisable for astronauts to touch down first on one of the big moons—say Ganymede—and plan the final approach from there.

Ganymede is some 665,000 miles from the planet itself—nearly three times farther away than our own Moon—and measures 3,200 miles across. Its terrain is probably very similar to our Moon's, but the daytime temperature is not thought to rise above minus 240 degrees Fahrenheit (minus 150 degrees Centigrade)—even when the Sun is shining.

It is another place where there are likely to be long periods of twilight, and it is also thought to be covered by a thick layer of frost or snow, with frozen gases encrusting the slopes and rocky plains.

Ganymede rotates at the same speed as it circles its mother

31. Jupiter, as it might look from its satellite Ganymede. The dark stripes can be clearly seen⟩

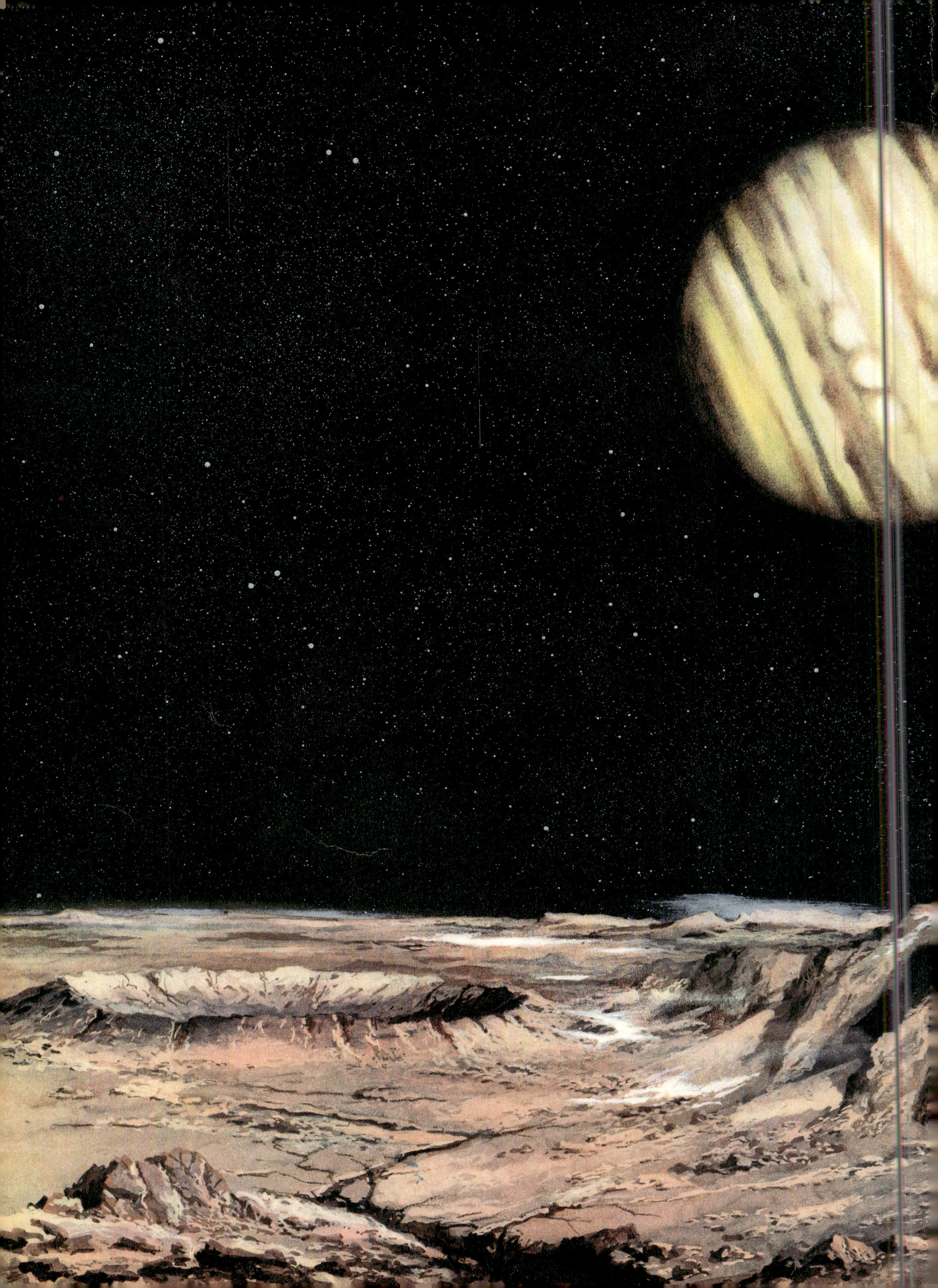

planet, thus always presenting Jupiter with the same face. From it, the view should be fascinating—probably more intriguing than any other we have seen so far in our travels.

All the surface features of Jupiter which are only detectable from Earth with a high-powered telescope should be visible from Ganymede with the naked eye: the intriguing dark stripes, for instance, which run parallel to the planet's equator; the various small spots and regions of light and dark shade which constantly seem to be changing their position; and the one big vivid spot in Jupiter's southern hemisphere which has given rise to so much speculation.

This Great Red Spot, as it is known, was noticed on Jupiter as long ago as 1664. It is located on the surface of the planet's atmosphere and varies in brightness and size. At its maximum it is immense: 30,000 miles long and 8,000 miles wide.

What could it possibly be?

Numerous observations have established that it is an area where the atmosphere is exceptionally dense—rather like the cold spot discovered on Venus by Mariner. One immediately jumps to the conclusion that it shrouds a tall mountain or mountain massif, such as the Tibetan plateau on Earth. But there is a snag to this explanation.

The spot sometimes shifts its position. Its latitude varies two or three degrees, and it moves a little in longitude also. It would not, therefore, seem to be tied to some fixed formation on Jupiter's crust, such as a volcano.

For the same reason, a theory which suggested that it could be a reflection in the clouds of a huge lake of lava below can be rejected. The most plausible explanation is that the Great Red Spot is composed of solid matter, floating in the lower strata of Jupiter's dense atmosphere. But if it *is* matter, it must be extremely light in weight.

Only when astronauts descend right down to it, or space probes pass close by, will we know for sure.

To travellers planning their last lap to Jupiter from Ganymede there are more immediate considerations. A day on Ganymede lasts the equivalent of 7 days 3 hours and 43 minutes—the time it takes to revolve around Jupiter. Half of that time will be spent in sunlight, half in total darkness. When it is dark it is colder than ever; but there are compensations.

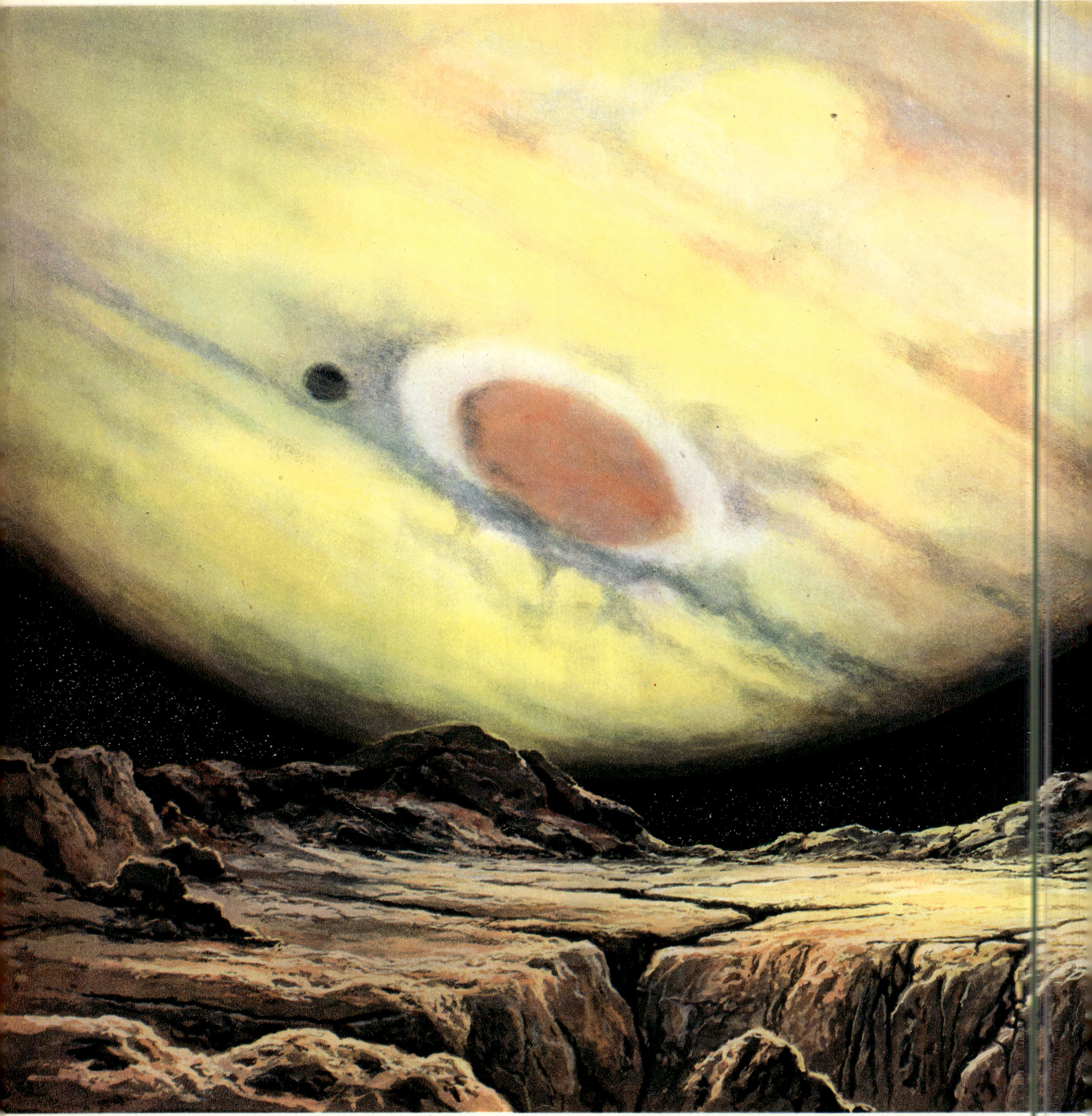

32. *'The one big vivid spot in Jupiter's southern hemisphere which has given rise to so much speculation'*

The phenomenon which occurs only rarely on Earth—a solar eclipse—is a frequent event on Ganymede because the mother planet often blocks off the Sun. But normally the sky there would not appear as black as on our Moon because there is an atmosphere—albeit a rare one. So some of the sunlight is scattered.

One of the things which might worry astronauts as they weigh up the approach to Jupiter itself is the possibility of a powerful gravitational field capturing their spaceship and tugging it violently towards the planet.

Since Jupiter has such a large mass one might logically reason that it could exert a strong pull on objects near by. In fact this is untrue: gravity there is unlikely to be much greater than the Earth's. The reason for this is that, despite its 86,800-mile diameter, the planet's density is little more than a fifth of Earth's.

What makes the planet appear so large is its atmosphere.

This is believed to consist—in its outermost layers, at least—of hydrogen mixed with some ammonia and marsh gas (methane). It is possible that clouds of frozen ammonia swirl about.

Below these, astronomers think, the atmosphere turns into a denser material more reminiscent of an ocean than a gas.

Some have claimed that a layer of solid ice lies under the hydrogen: others that there is no nucleus of rock to Jupiter, but rather an ever-densifying mass of hydrogen, forced inwards by pressure. If the latter is true, at the core of Jupiter is likely to lie a very rare metal indeed—the metal of hydrogen. To squeeze hydrogen so tightly that it turns into a metal is one of the physicist's dreams, because in that state a colossal amount of energy could be stored in a very small space.

One small bar of metallic hydrogen, for example, might contain enough latent power to send a spaceship millions of miles into the heavens, if only it could be fashioned in the first place.

Certainly there are good grounds for believing that pressure builds up dramatically as you go deeper and deeper into Jupiter's atmosphere. About 6,000 miles below the clouds, it is calculated to be one million times greater than at sea level on Earth: and with a rise in pressure goes a rise in temperature.

On the outer 'skin' of the atmosphere it is thought to be minus 200 degrees Fahrenheit (minus 130 degrees Centigrade). But under the layers it is thought to rise well above boiling point.

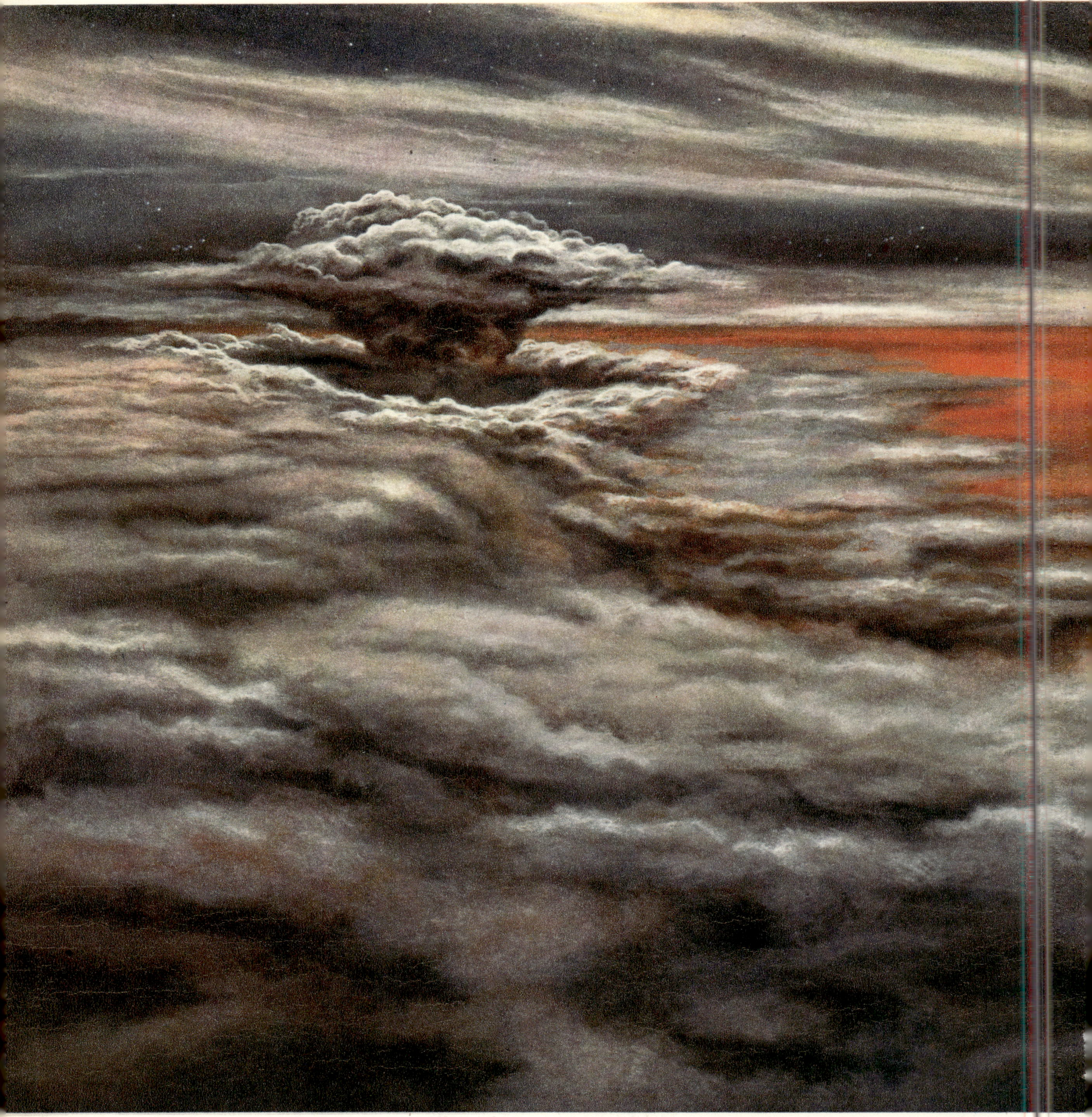

33. '*Huge, mushroom-shaped clouds would billow to a tremendous height over Jupiter, in the manner of a hydrogen bomb test on Earth*'

There is a tremendous aura of violence about Jupiter. This is mainly due to the turbulence of the clouds.

Despite its bulk, the planet rotates once in less than ten hours. This spinning motion has a startling effect on the gas layers above. The rate of spin is fastest at the equator, and slowest at the poles. Consequently the atmosphere seems to form a series of belts, each of which travels at a different speed according to how far north or south of the equator it may be, and parallel to it.

Some of the belts are light in colour, others dark; some are thick, others thin. The effect is rather like looking at a cross-section of terrestrial rock layers, except that the belts seem to oscillate vertically as well as horizontally.

Colours are discernible in the whirling belts—red, brown and greenish hues sometimes clustering to form a spot which stands out against the background, as in the case of the Great Red Spot. These colours may be due to light metals, such as calcium and sodium, dissolving in liquid ammonia.

In the opinion of some astronomers, movement of the spots and fluctuations in the belts can be attributed to occasional eruptions of dust and smoke particles from Jupiter's lower strata into the outer atmosphere.

Such eruptions could be caused by gigantic explosions in the planet's interior.

Huge, mushroom-shaped clouds would billow to a tremendous height in the manner of a hydrogen bomb test on Earth; the gases would then freeze, crystallising rapidly and creating a light-coloured spot in the upper atmosphere.

The Great Red Spot may well be the result of one such massive explosion, the debris having remained permanently suspended.

There are additional grounds for thinking that eruptions cause the spots. If Jupiter's atmosphere contained *only* hydrogen, methane and ammonia crystals, one would expect it to look as dull and uniform as, say, Venus's. Since it is far from uniform one concludes that foreign matter is sometimes injected.

We have a vivid picture, then, of Jupiter as a large, twirling mass, hostile in the extreme, blanketed by dense layers of eddying gas and patrolled incessantly by twelve faithful moons beyond which it would seem thoroughly unwise for Man to venture—even assuming he had the power to do so.

How life could survive on Jupiter is impossible to imagine.

SATURN

Strike out from Jupiter still farther into the solar system and you come to Saturn, another of the major planets and unique in our sky. It is smaller than Jupiter—a mere 75,000 miles wide—and is patrolled by nine moons, one of which is the biggest satellite yet detected. But Saturn's chief claim to fame is its rings—flat, light-reflecting bands which completely encircle the planet around its midriff.

More about these later.

The planet is quite unlike our Earth. Nobody is certain of what it is made, but theories suggest it is either tightly-packed cold gas or rock thickly covered with ice. About one thing *everybody* agrees—that it is a bitterly cold place. Temperatures are unlikely to climb above minus 120 degrees Fahrenheit.

One of the problems in deciding the nature of Saturn is that no man has ever seen its surface. It comes no closer to us than 742,000,000 miles and it is covered with a dense atmosphere. This certainly contains quantities of hydrogen, methane and ammonia gases, but the ammonia might be there in crystalline form as well.

As with Jupiter, the atmosphere is whipped into the form of dark-coloured belts by the planet's rotation, and spots can sometimes be observed there too, suggesting storms.

Saturn spins quickly. This fact is obvious from the planet's shape. It looks like a pumpkin—7,000 miles fatter around the equator than around the poles. If you stood on the equator you would go round once in 10 hours 14 minutes.

The swirling clouds of gas pick up sunlight in a strange way, making the equator look yellow and the polar regions green.

Since so little is known about the surface of Saturn it would be wise for astronauts to land first on one of its moons. These are called Mimas, Enceladus, Tethis, Dione, Rhea, Titan, Hyperion, Iapetus and Phoebe.

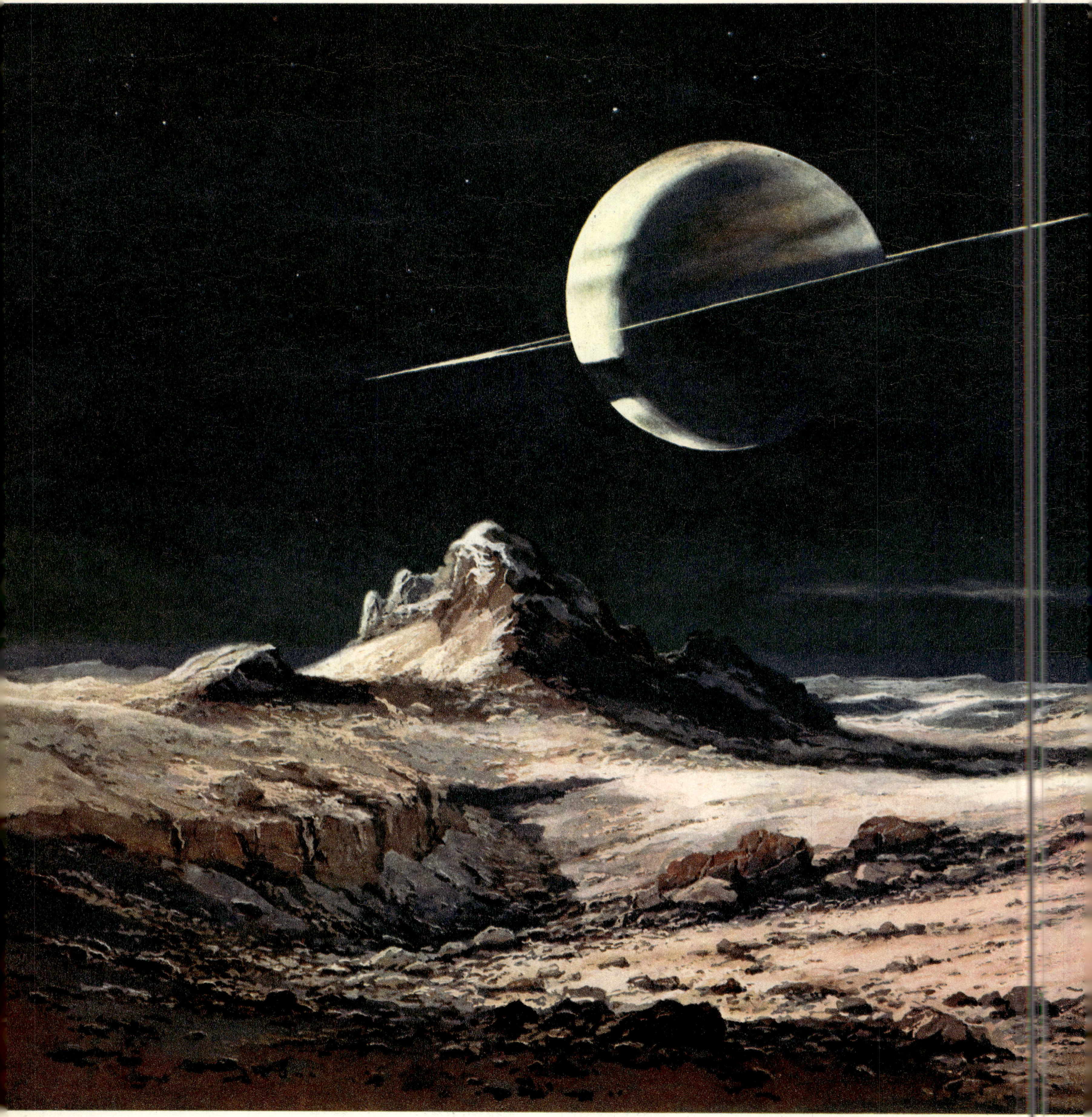

34. *Saturn — The Ringed Planet*

The biggest—Titan—has an atmosphere.

Titan orbits its mother planet at an average distance of 760,000 miles. Its surface is probably similar to that of Ganymede—Jupiter's largest moon—but the haze over it is thicker. This haze is composed of ammonia and methane—gases which would have no appeal to visitors from Earth—and the ground is likely to be covered with ammonia 'snow' as well. The temperature drops as low as minus 330 degrees Fahrenheit (minus 200 degrees Centigrade).

A day on Titan is equivalent to 15 days 22 hours and 41 minutes on Earth and it is another of those moons which always keeps the same face pointed towards its 'mother'.

A day on Mimas by contrast—Saturn's nearest moon—lasts less than an Earth day, and from there the big planet appears to go through 'phases' in rapid succession.

At one point Saturn vanishes completely; 5 hours 39 minutes later it reveals its first quarter, and after that it is 'full' once more.

Seen from any of Saturn's moons, the Sun would appear a small but extremely bright body; the Earth would only be visible through a powerful telescope.

From Mimas, an astronaut would get a beautiful view of Saturn. The disc would seem immense, and girdling it—with the sun glowing on them—would be those fascinating rings.

They were first discovered in 1655. Up till that time most astronomers—including the great Galileo—had believed Saturn to be in three pieces. Some had suggested that the planet had projections like handles attached to it, but nobody could suggest why.

Then a Dutchman named Huygens invented a more powerful telescope and was able to announce to the world that Saturn was a ringed disc.

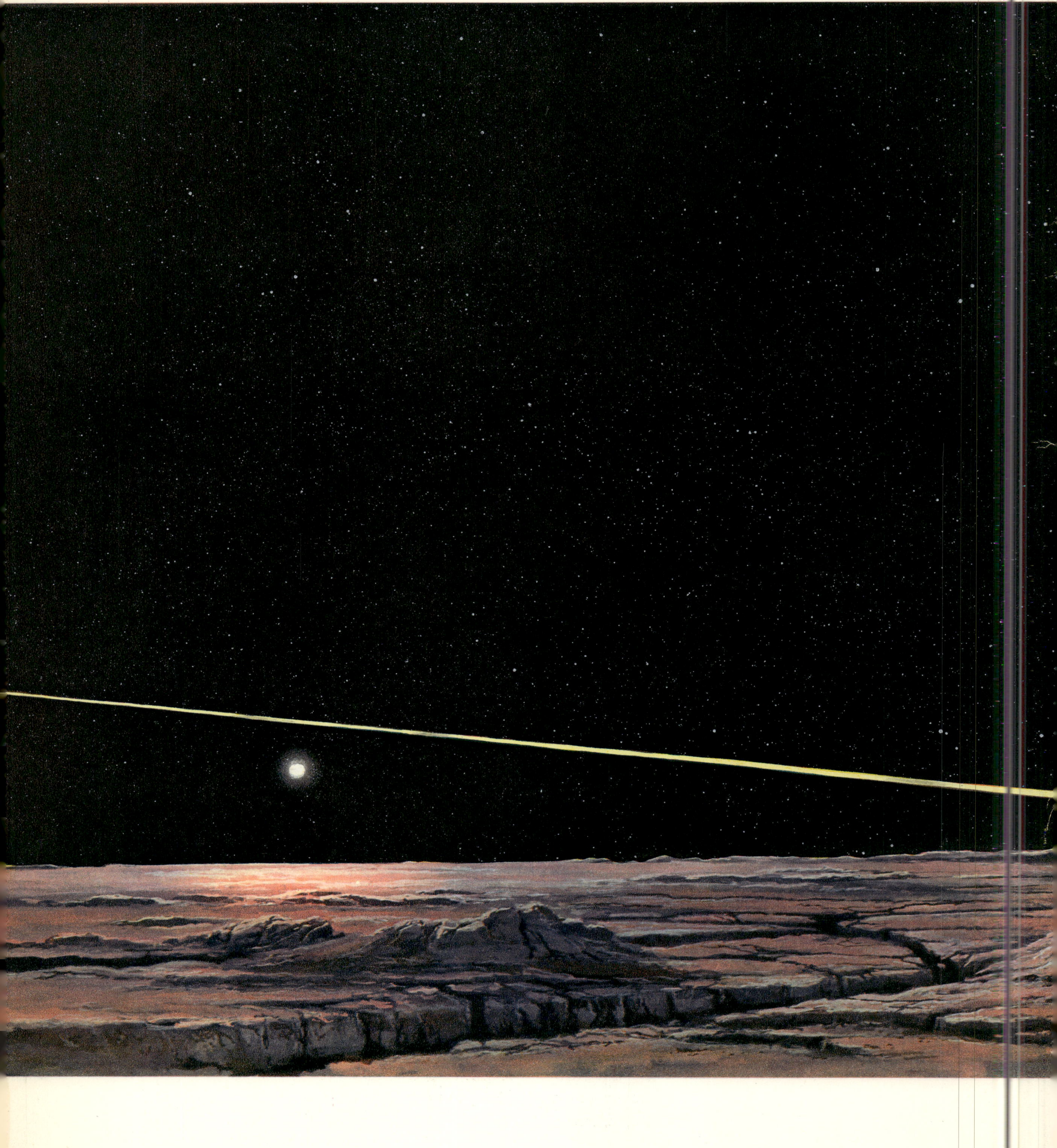

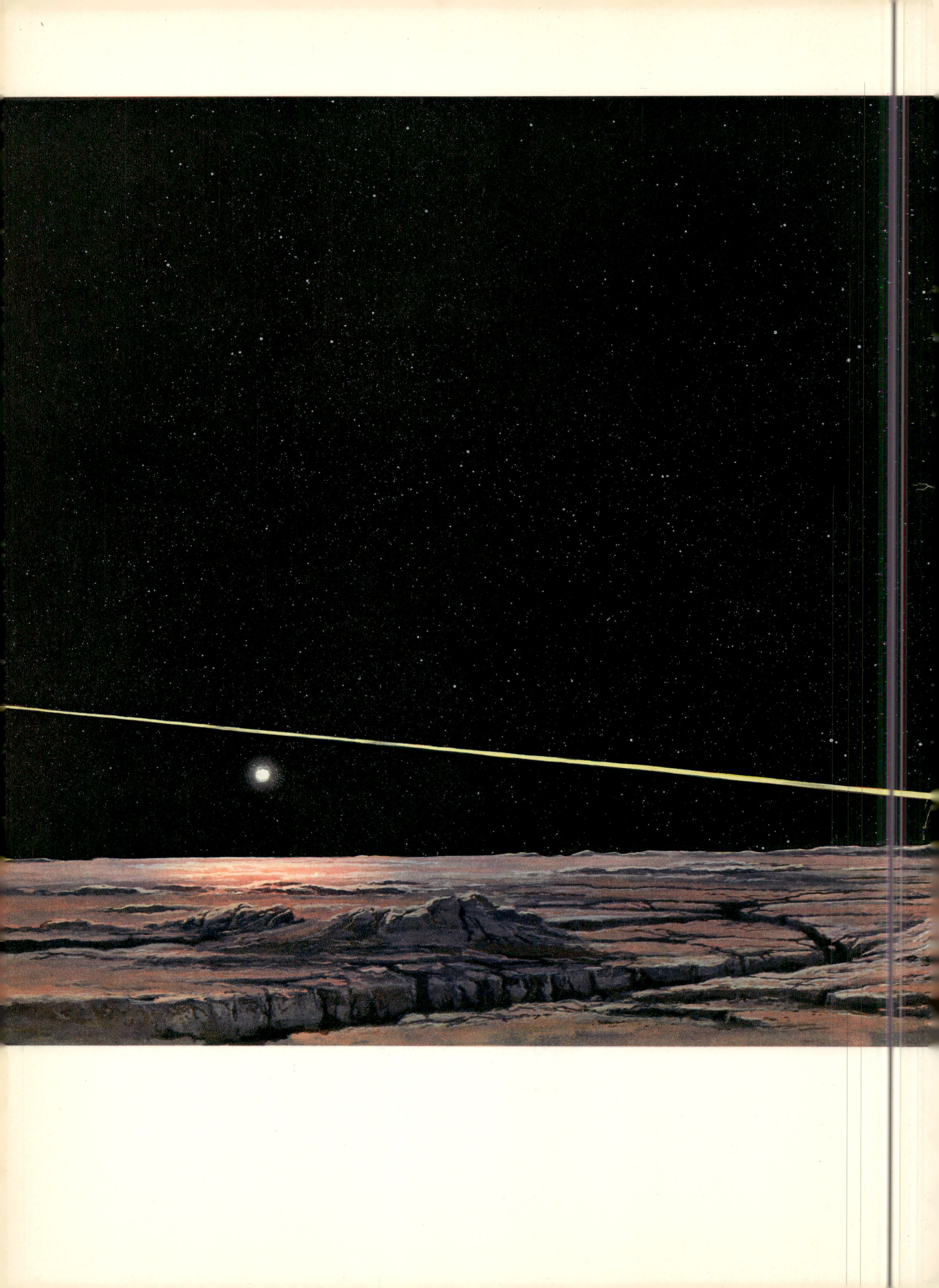

35. *'Saturn's chief claim to fame is its rings — flat, light-reflecting bands which encircle the planet'*

He believed there to be only one ring, about 175,000 miles in diameter. But in 1675 a French astronomer named Cassini noticed that a line divided the ring in two. To this day the dark gap is called 'Cassini's Division', and at times a star can be seen shining clearly through it.

About 1850 a third, much fainter ring was detected—inside the other two—and this is now known as the *crêpe* ring.

The rings give Saturn the appearance of a fictional 'flying saucer', skimming around the Sun.

From Earth they seem to open out at times—narrowing to a thin line every 15 years or so. It would be logical to think that they are flat, solid sheets of some material; but Saturn is so big and its gravity so powerful, therefore, that any solid layer would be tugged to pieces rapidly.

The most recent view is that they are made up of millions of separate fragments. This is borne out by the fact that they whirl around Saturn at different speeds, with the outermost ring going more slowly than the rest.

The whole system is no more than 10 miles thick, but whether it stretches right down to the surface of the planet is a matter for debate. Some hold that the crêpe ring actually touches Saturn's clouds and that particles from it spiral down into the atmosphere, subjecting the equator to a constant bombardment; others say there is a clear demarcation line to it.

The rings contain light and dark areas, indicating that the density of the matter in them varies; but the shadow cast by the whole system across Saturn's middle looks remarkably uniform.

How did they originate?

Most astronomers today accept the idea that they are the remnants of a tenth or eleventh moon which once orbited Saturn but which was literally torn to shreds by gravity when it came too close. But there is no reliable evidence.

36. 'The most recent view is that Saturn's rings are made up of millions of separate fragments' >

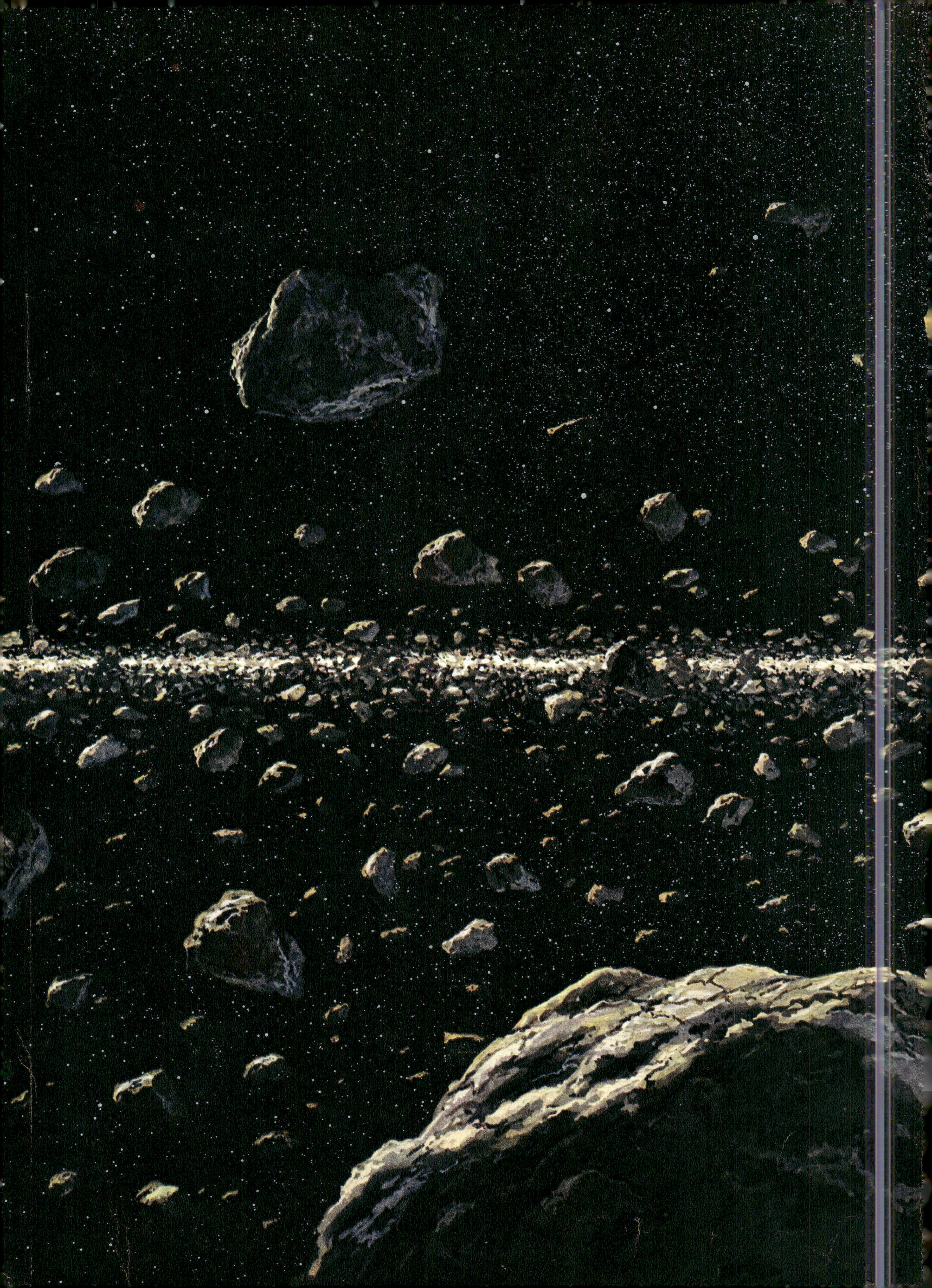

An interesting feature of the rings is that they reflect much more light than is usual from fragments of meteors or shattered moons. This has led to the suggestion that they are, in fact, sparkling ice crystals or frost-coated specks of dust. They may be surrounded by frozen gas-like matter inside the nucleus of a comet.

The particles vary considerably in size. In the inner or crêpe ring they probably measure no more than four-thousandths of an inch across, but in the outer belt—known as Ring A—they appear to be anything from one to ten yards across. One group of astronomers recently claimed to have measured some with a diameter of more than a hundred yards, but it is estimated that if you compressed all the matter in the rings it would add up to no more than a millionth of the mass of Saturn itself.

The only other thing we know for sure is that the fragments congregate most thickly over the planet's equator, but why, is another mystery.

I mentioned earlier that spots are seen from time to time on Saturn. They disappear rapidly, but the most prominent was observed in 1933. It looked like a big white blob, situated just to the right of Saturn's centre and just above the line of rings. So far nobody has explained it.

In conclusion, then, it can be said that Saturn is a most attractive and interesting planet to gaze at through a telescope, but that its attractions are likely to diminish in the eyes of Man in direct ratio to the closeness of his approach to it.

A large sign ASTRONAUTS BEWARE should be nailed to it.

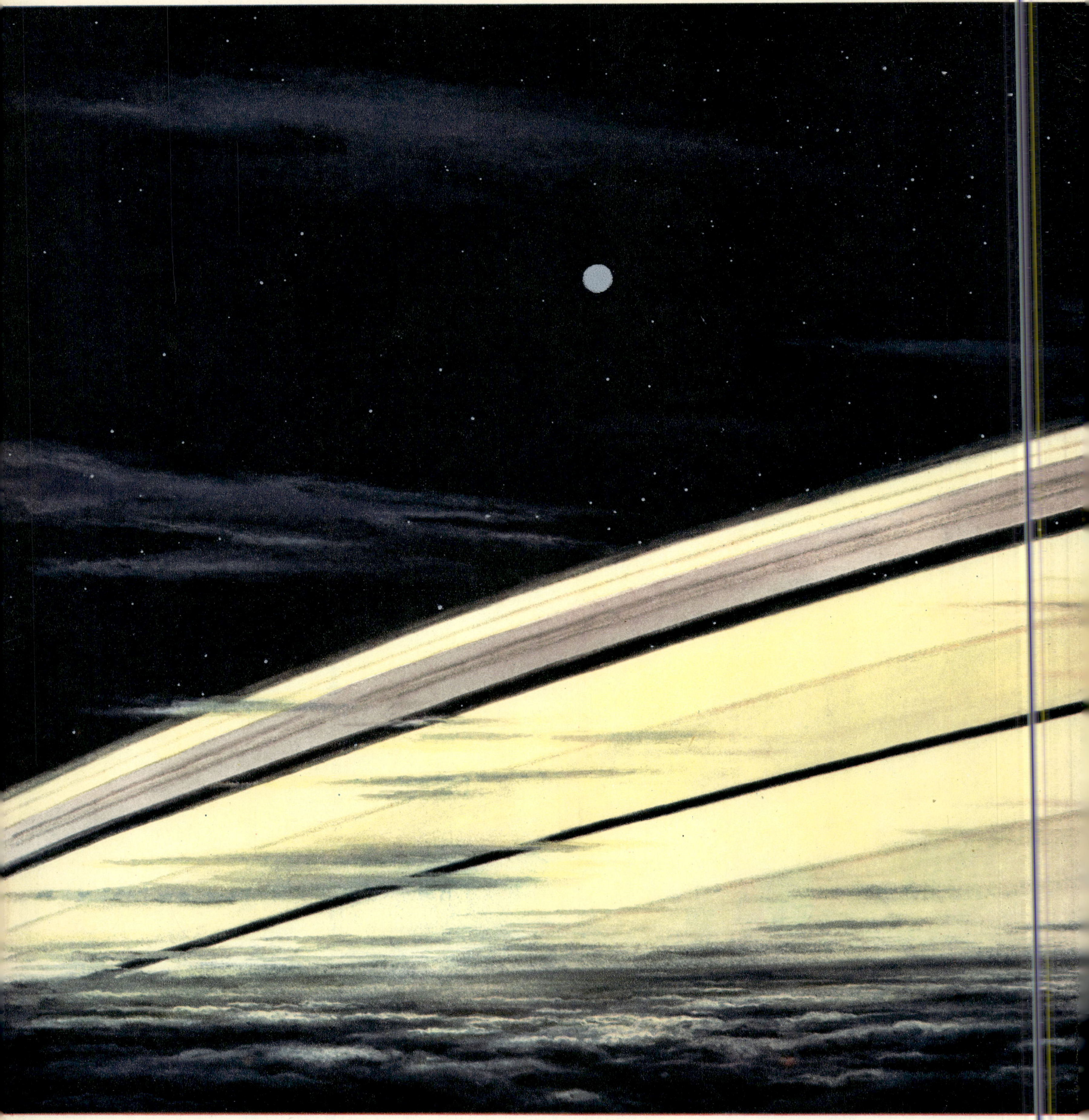

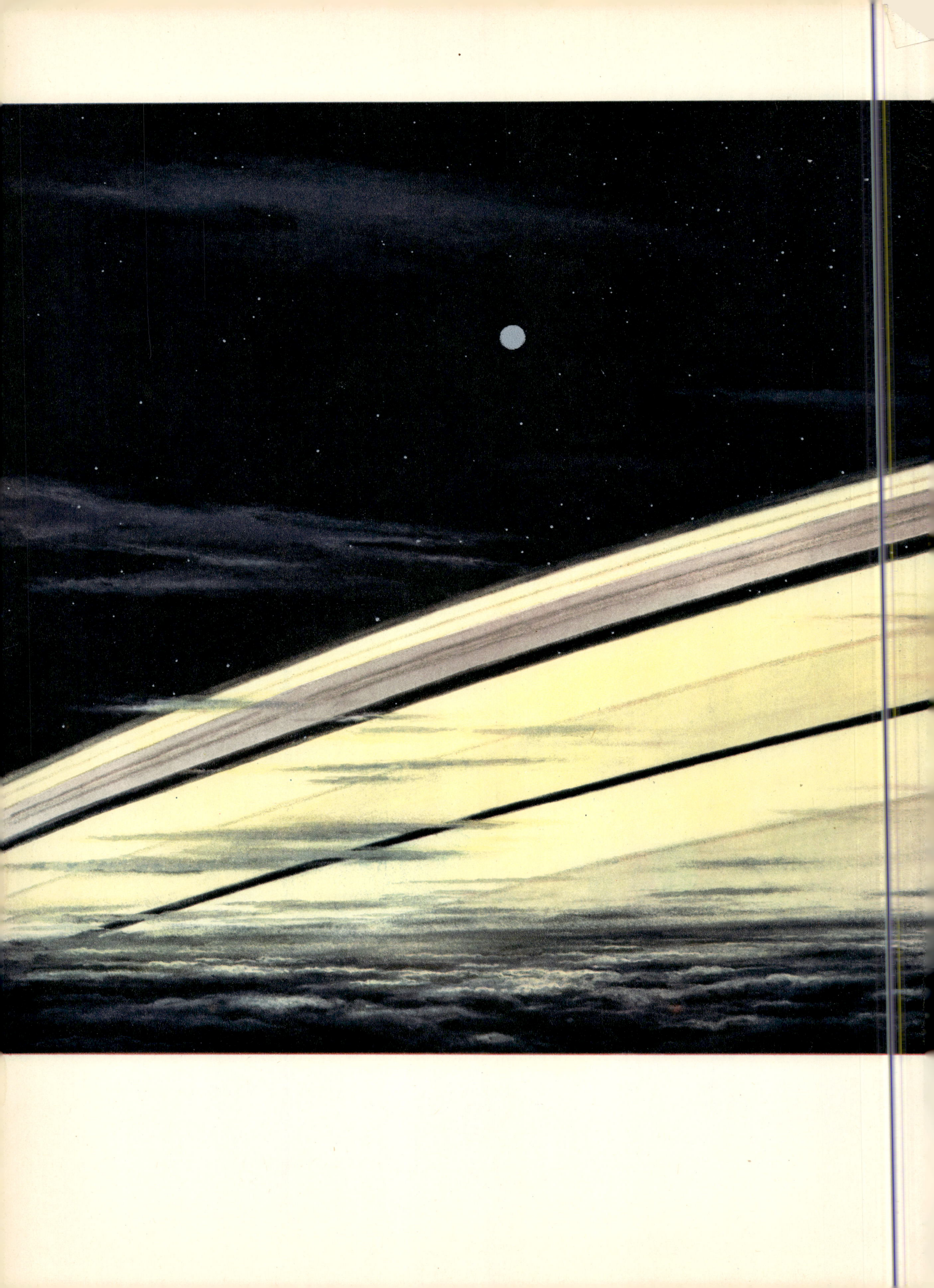

37. *The rings of Saturn, as they might appear from the surface of the planet*

URANUS

To anyone standing on Uranus, the Solar System would seem to contain remarkably few objects. There would be the planet's own five satellites; there would be Neptune and Saturn; Jupiter would appear as a very dim star; but the rest of the planets—Earth, Mercury, Venus, Mars and Pluto—would have vanished.

Comets—even ones fairly close to Uranus—would not be visible either, despite their trailing 'tails'.

All this is due to the fact that Uranus is an average of 1,800,000,000 miles away from the Sun. Little sunlight reaches it, or the region of space around it. The faraway 'inner' planets simply blend into the Sun's disc.

The disc itself would look no bigger than a sixpence at a distance of 10 yards but its radiation would still damage the eyes.

Uranus was discovered accidentally in 1781. Until that year it had always been taken for a star. Then an astronomer named Herschel, who happened to be studying a particular area of the sky, noticed that it was orbiting the Sun.

Today our telescopes show it as a greenish ball with faint traces of belts similar to those on Jupiter. Its atmosphere is thought to conceal a thick layer of ice and contain mainly hydrogen and methane gas. The temperature on its crust has been measured and reads minus 90 degrees Centigrade—brutally cold.

It is colder still on Uranus's five moons, which have been given the names of Miranda, Ariel, Umbriel, Titania and Oberon. The biggest of these—Titania—is estimated to be 600 miles wide.

Uranus itself is about 14½ times the size of the Earth and revolves around its axis every 10 hours or so.

It has, however, a special distinction; it is a planet lying on its side. Its axis—that is, the imaginary rod connecting its poles—points almost directly to the Sun, while its equator is nearly perpendicular.

This has the effect of making 'seasons' on Uranus quite different from those we know on Earth. People living (if such a thing were possible) at the planet's poles would face winters and summers—or nights and days, if you prefer—which last 42 Earth years.

Imagine 15,330 days of maximum temperatures well below freezing, no food to eat, only hydrogen or marsh gas to breathe, and a dingy gloom all around you!

Would *you* like to go to Uranus?

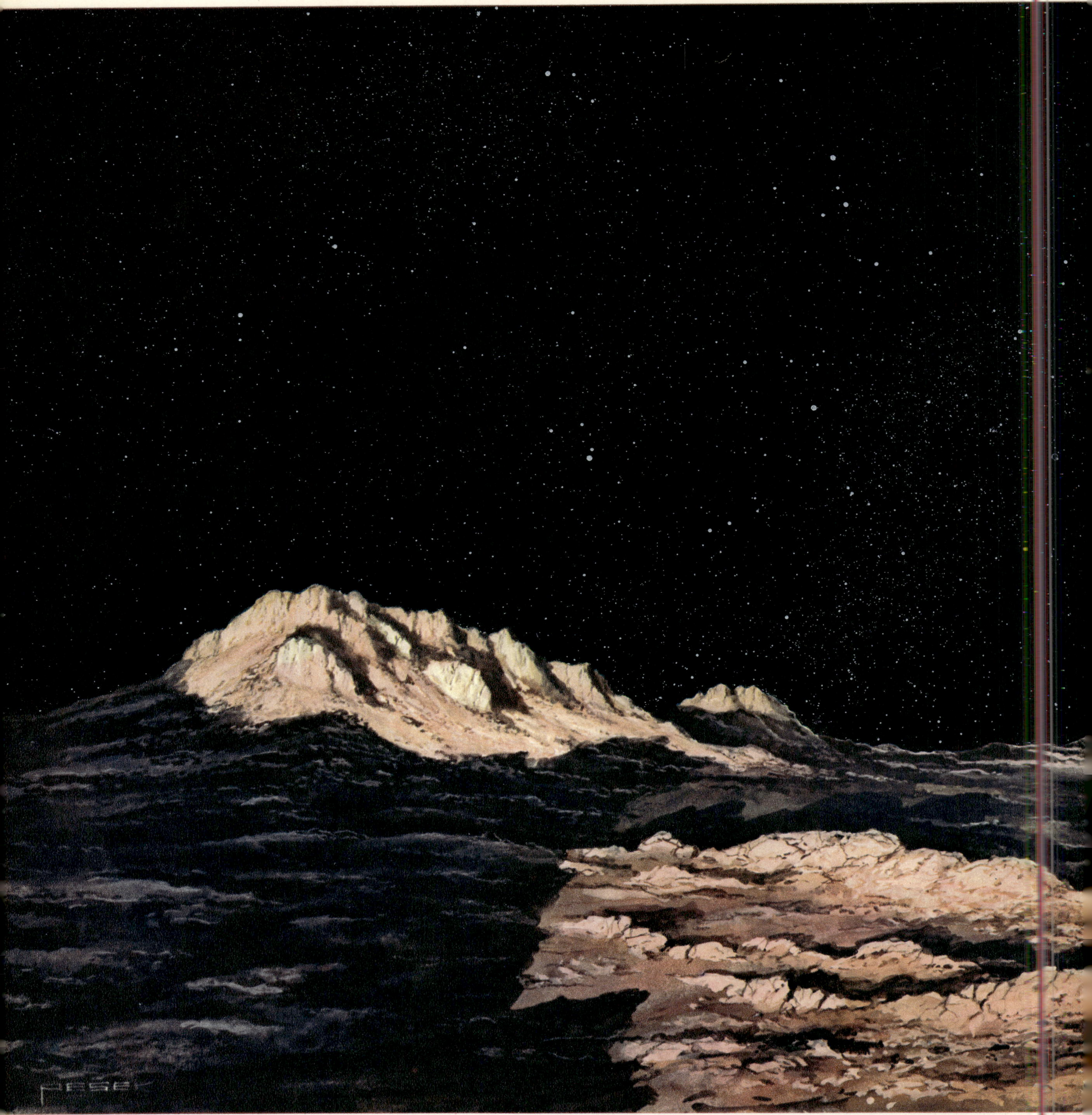

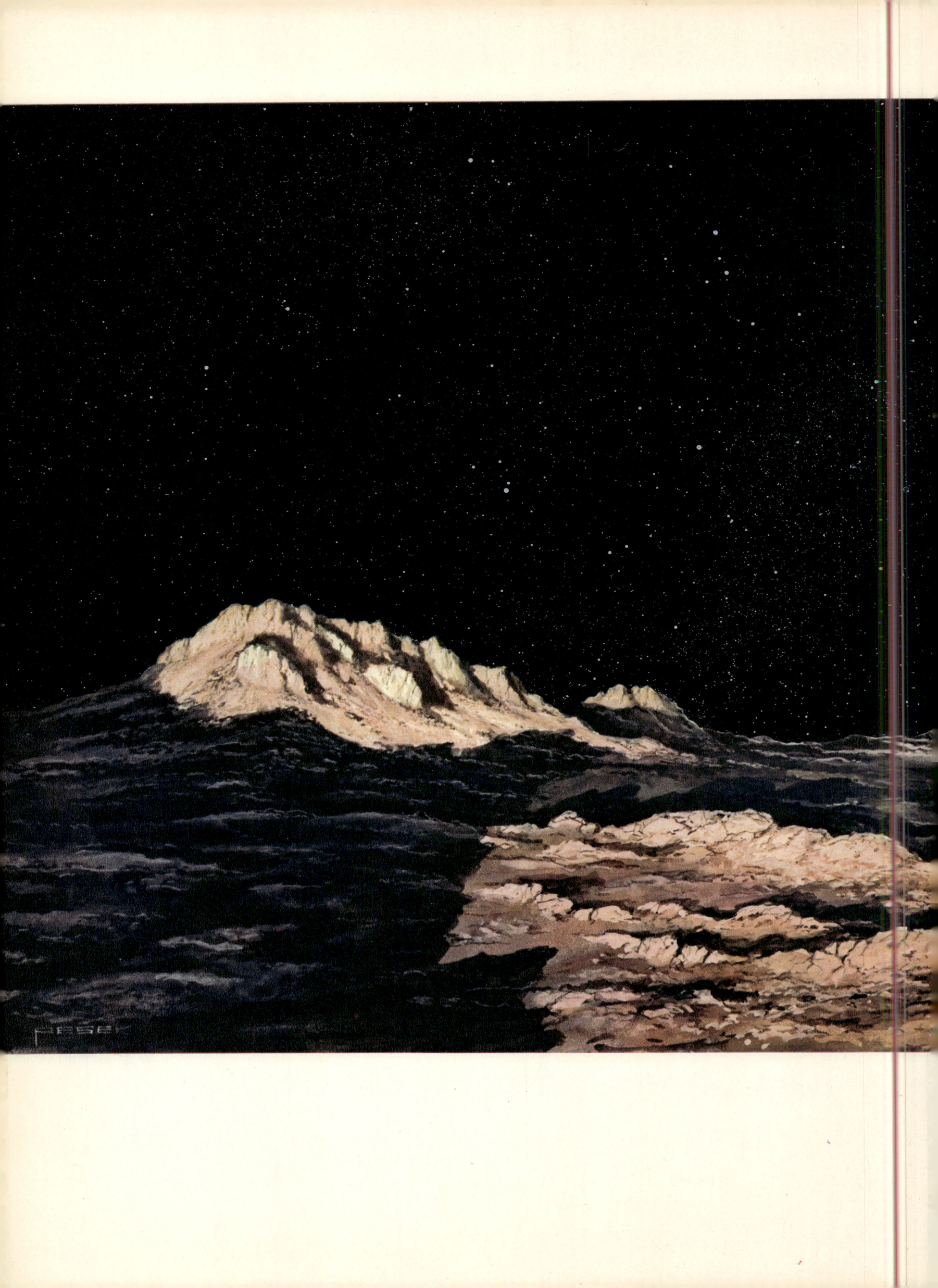

38. *Uranus, as it might look from its satellite Oberon*

NEPTUNE

The eighth and next-to-last planet in our Solar System might well be called Uranus's twin. In fact it is Neptune, and it was discovered in 1846 as a result of a remarkable piece of international collaboration.

For over 60 years the presence of Uranus had been known to astronomers and its orbit carefully calculated. The calculations had made due allowance for the slight pulls exerted on the planet by its neighbours, notably Saturn and Jupiter. But despite this Uranus kept on turning up in the 'wrong' place in the sky.

The error was only small but it was recurrent. *Something*—some unseen force—was tugging at Uranus, in addition to the known planets. What could it be?

By 1845 a young Cambridge scientist called John Adams had worked out that it must be yet another planet. He had worked out, too, where the mysterious body must be.

Simultaneously, but independently, a French mathematician named Le Verrier had reached the same conclusion.

Adams sent his predictions to the Astronomer Royal in England, but he was too slow to react. Le Verrier sent *his* calculations to the Berlin Observatory in Germany. Twenty-four hours later, astronomers there pointed their telescopes at the spot designated by the Frenchman and sure enough located Neptune.

Today both Adams and Le Verrier are given equal credit for the discovery.

Neptune is invisible to us without a telescope because of its great distance from the Sun—an average of 2,793 million miles.

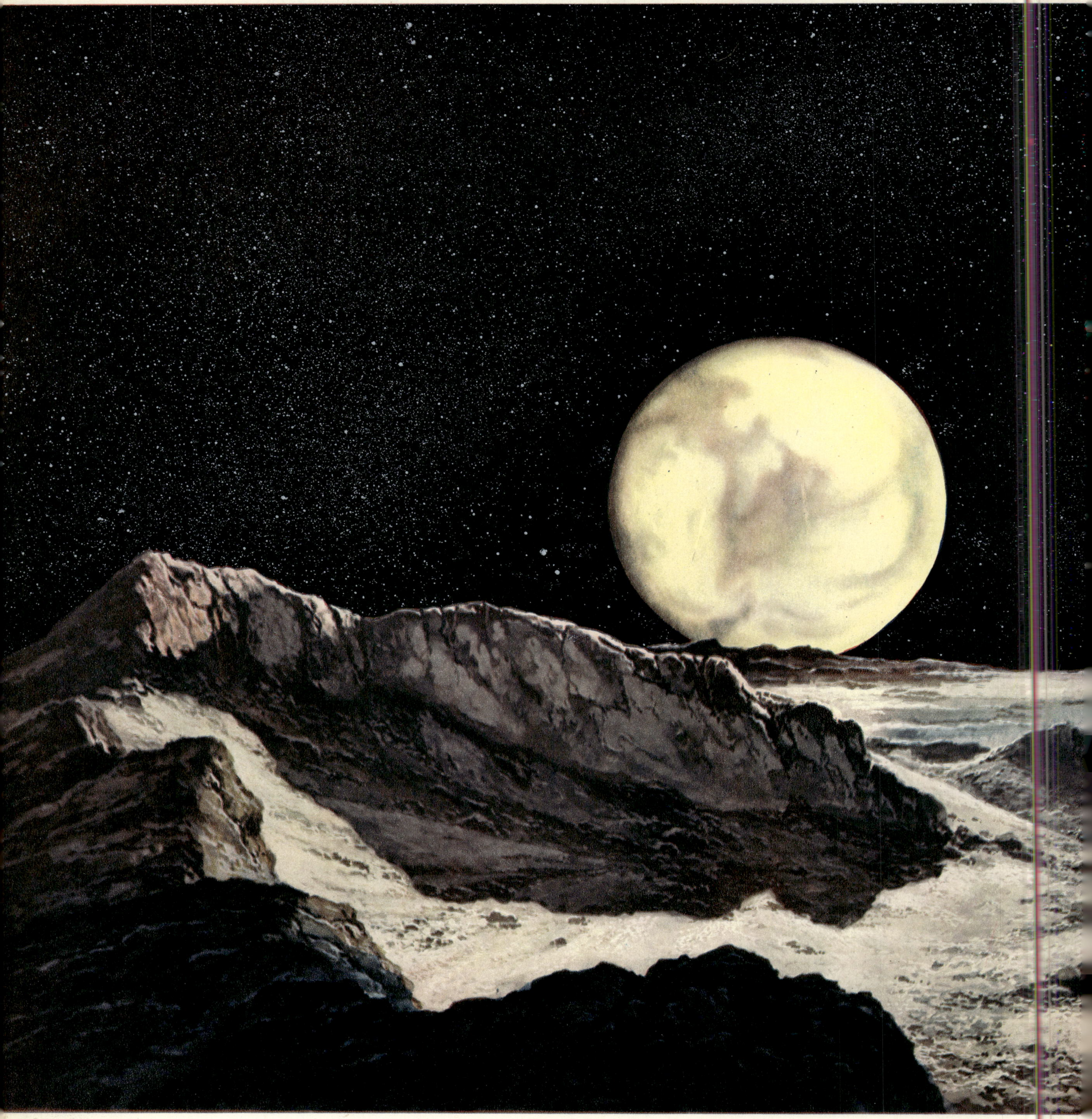

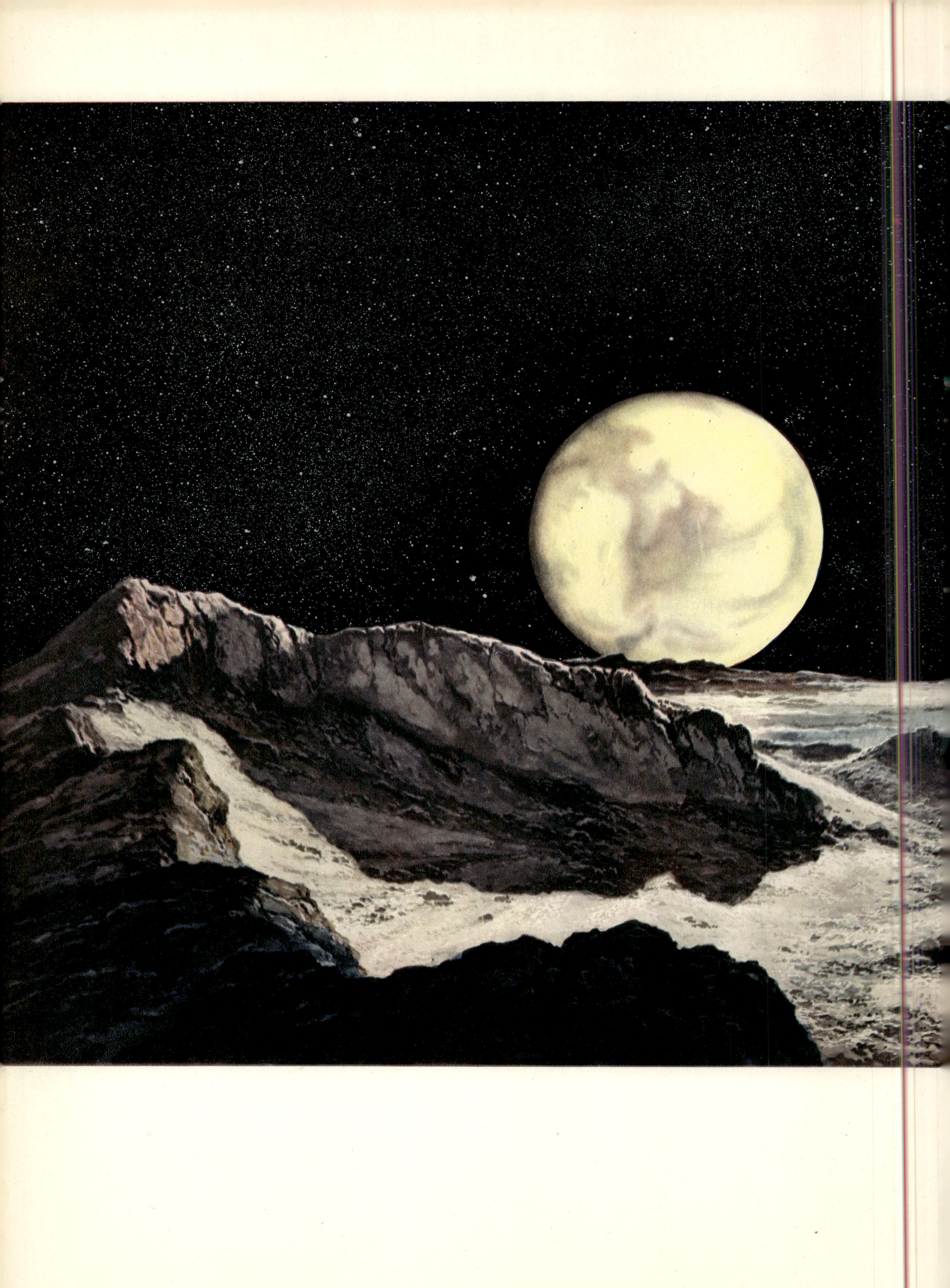

39. *Neptune — is it solid like this?*

But it is a large planet with a mass more than 17 times greater than the Earth's. Like all the other big objects it revolves rapidly about its axis. Some calculations show this to be 12 hours $43^{1}/_{2}$ minutes, while others suggest 15 hours 40 minutes.

It takes 164.78 years to go round the Sun, and from it that fiery disc must look very small. Neptune is a very cold place indeed.

It has two moons—one noted within a few weeks of the planet's own discovery, but the other not for another 103 years. These satellites have been given the titles Triton and Nereid.

Triton probably measures 3,000 miles in diameter, but Nereid is a much smaller lump, swinging around Neptune in a highly eccentric way.

The main planet appears as a blue disc to us on Earth, with some irregular spots on it. Spectroscopes indicate that it has an atmosphere of hydrogen and methane, but there may be other gases as well—possibly nitrogen and helium.

There are two conflicting theories about Neptune's origin—one suggesting that it has a solid heart enclosed in ice, the other that its middle is volatile and composed of hydrogen which has condensed.

Unfortunately, no surface details whatsoever are visible from Earth, and so the only advice one can give prospective visitors is 'Wrap up well—and go warily'.

A thorough, preliminary reconnaissance is advisable.

PLUTO

Two photographs of the night sky, placed side by side, gave Man the knowledge that a *ninth* planet existed in his Solar System.

Up till 1930 he had believed there were only eight. Two decades earlier than that, an American astronomer named Percy Lowell, star-gazing from his observatory at Flagstaff, Arizona, had noticed that some unseen force was disturbing the predicted orbit of Uranus. He made due allowance for Neptune's gravity having an effect, but this still did not seem enough to account for the whole 'wobble'.

He reasoned that another large body must lie beyond Uranus, tugging away at the big planet. He plotted the position of this body in 1915. But he died before he could find it.

His calculations were taken up by a fellow astronomer named Tombaugh, who trained a camera on the relevant part of the sky. He took pictures at different times—then compared them.

Suddenly he saw that one of the twinkling 'stars' had moved. It was, in fact, the missing planet. It is an interesting tribute to Percy Lowell that the name Pluto begins with his initials.

Tombaugh's discovery may have been an amazing stroke of luck. For the planet would appear to be too small to affect the great Uranus. However, some scientists wonder if there is not more to Pluto than meets the eye.

Through telescopes the planet seems only a fraction larger than Mars, yet its mass is calculated to be almost as great as the Earth's. This, if true, could mean that it had an unbelievably high density—about 50 grams of solid material to every cubic centimetre of space. We know of no other matter which is so dense, so there is a suspicion that we may be measuring Pluto's diameter incorrectly.

Pluto seems to have a shiny surface, which may reflect sunlight rather like a curved mirror. If this is so, then we are only seeing the brightest part of the planet's disc in the sky—the centre—and this would make Pluto appear smaller than it is.

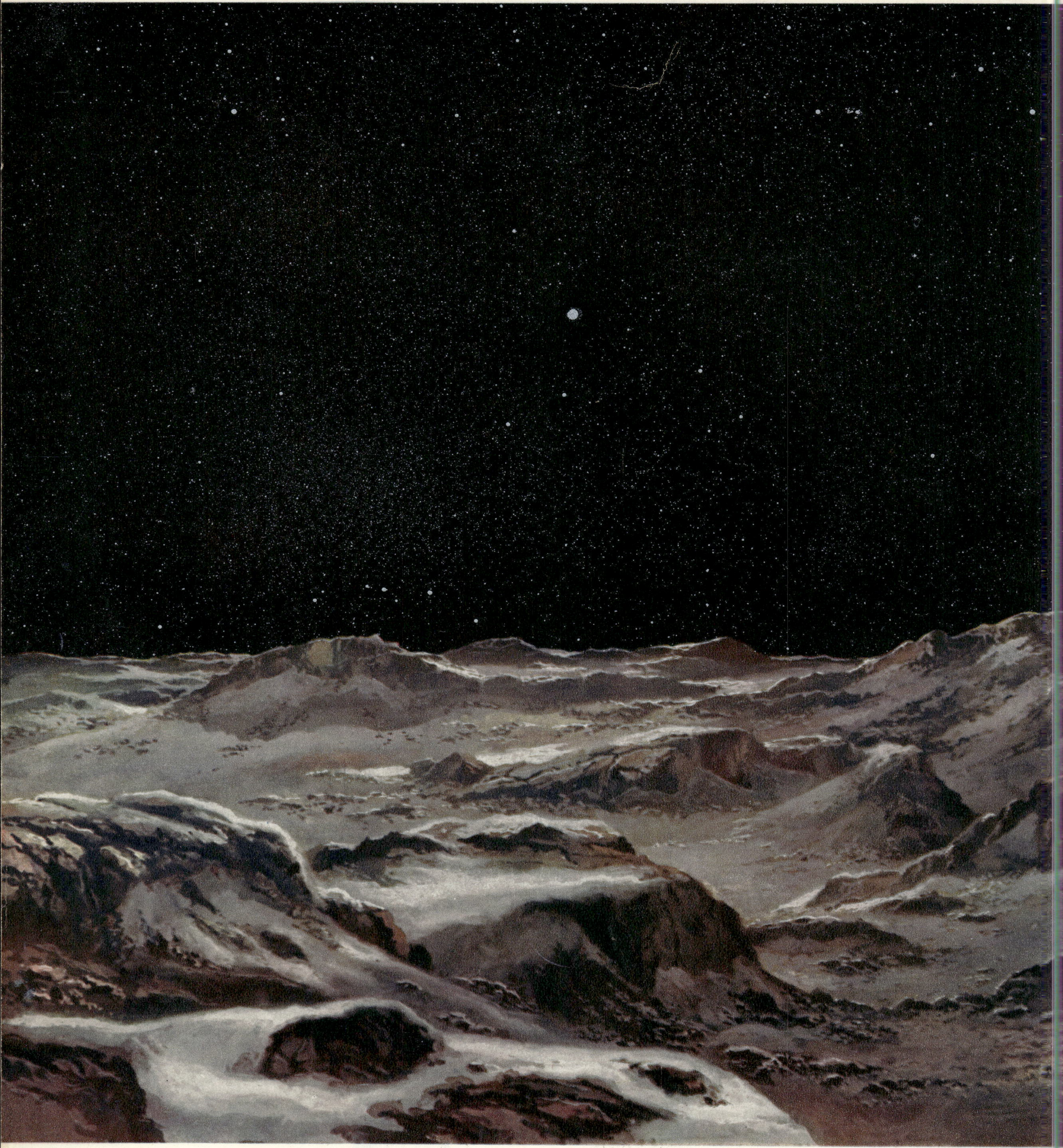

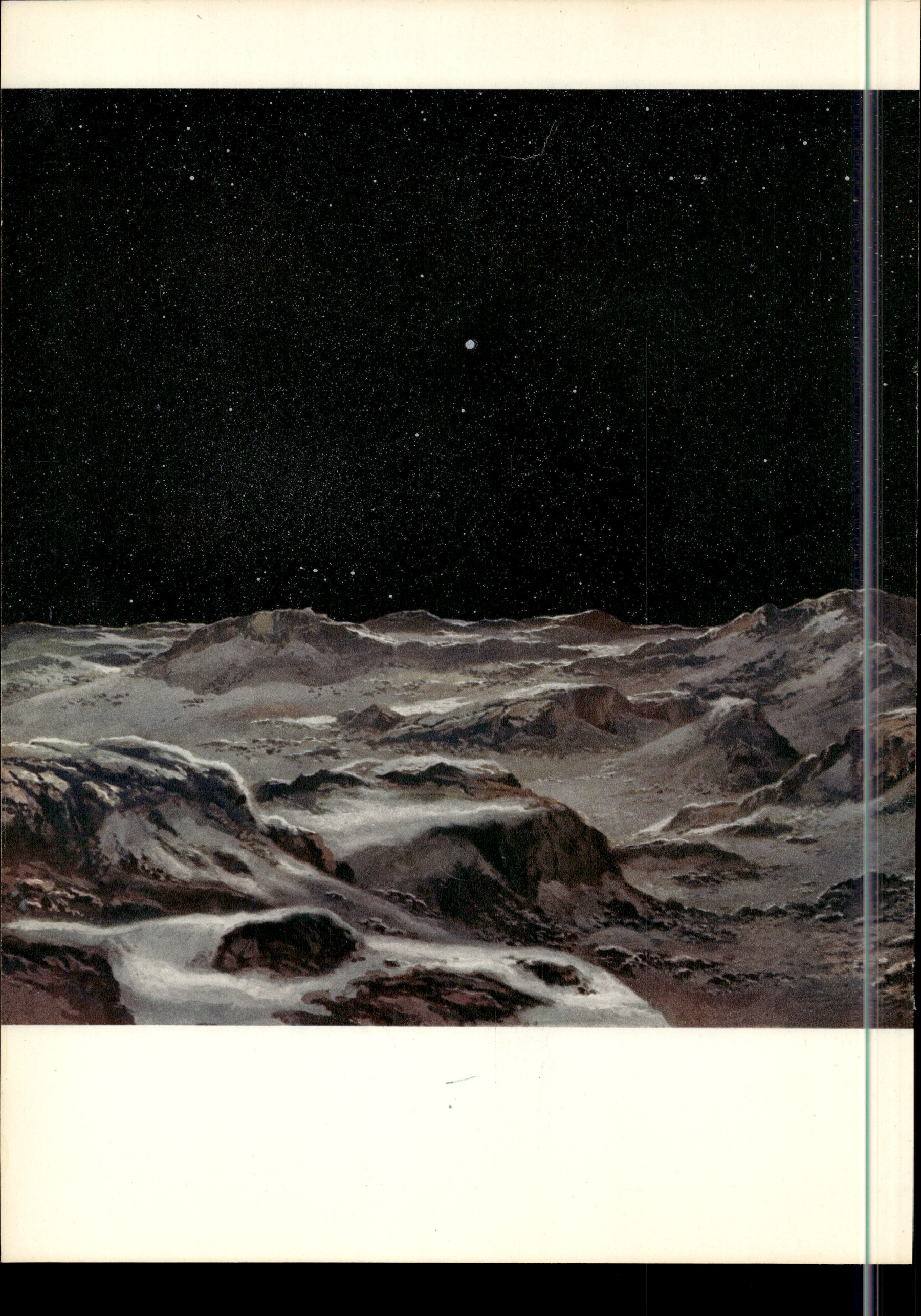

40. *Pluto is another extremely cold planet*

It is another extremely cold planet. Its average temperature is minus 350 degrees Fahrenheit (minus 230 degrees Centigrade), lower than the freezing point of most known gases. Only hydrogen would survive in a volatile state there; any other gases would form a frosty layer.

It might well be this that causes the mirror effect.

Unfortunately, Pluto can only be seen through a powerful telescope, and even then it is very faint. Therefore it is hard to give an accurate judgment. But it is strange for an apparently small planet to be out amongst the 'superiors'. This has led theoreticians to suggest that it is not a planet but satellite that was pulled out of the mother planet's influence by some mysterious force.

Its orbit actually crosses that of Neptune, and is in the shape of a large ellipse. Its mean distance from the Sun is 3,666 miles and it takes about 248 years to go round it.

Observations tell us that a day and a night there would be the equivalent of nearly a week on Earth.

Nobody is quite certain what kind of atmosphere surrounds the planet except that it is bound to be a very thin one. And because of the extreme cold it holds few charms for visiting spacemen.

Even if one stood on the surface of Pluto, the stars in the heavens would seem no closer. For by cosmic standards Pluto is but a stone's throw from the Sun and the Earth, while the rest of the bodies in the black sky are trillions of miles farther out.

Man would, therefore, be more conscious than ever of his puniness. He would have braved the hurtling rocks, braved the radiation, braved the possibility of a total failure inside his portable world of air—and yet have apparently come no closer to the edge of the Universe. And he would face a mammoth journey back. For the trip from Pluto down to Earth would take about 20 years.